PUBLISHER'S NOTE

We had a secretary here, briefly, who answered the phone one day when Walt Kelly was calling and said in a sprightly voice, "Yes, Mr. Kelly, is it about anything?"

The same question could be applied with effect to the great majority of the 12,000 books published this year in America.

Trying it on with this one, the answer appears to be, if you are in Congress or a lawyer, in the affirmative. Otherwise, yes. It isn't about everything, just some things. That's why it is called The Incompleat Pogo. The Compleat Pogo will have to wait for a few thousand years when we know the answers to everything instead of just getting around, as we are now, to a foggy idea of what some of the questions are.

Other Books by Walt Kelly

POGO

I GO POGO

UNCLE POGO SO-SO STORIES

THE POGO PAPERS

THE POGO STEPMOTHER GOOSE

The
INCOMPLEAT
POGO

by
Walt Kelly

SIMON AND SCHUSTER
NEW YORK

FOURTH PRINTING
MANUFACTURED IN THE UNITED STATES OF AMERICA
PRINTED BY WILLIAM KONECKY ASSOCIATES, INC., N. Y.
BOUND BY F. M. CHARLTON COMPANY, N. Y.

For my father

The poets have muddied all the little fountains.
Yet do not my strong eyes know you, far house? . . .

Antara, 6th century.

CONTENTS

CHAPTER
1

From Here On Down It's
Uphill All The Way

I ACCEPTS YO' *REE-MARK* AS THE **CRUDITY** OF A **IGNORHINOCERUS!** —— *MY SAKES!* POGO SURE PACKED IN SOME **AWFUL** **TASTELESS** GRUB.

YOU IS EATIN' YO' OWN HAT.

I IS HAD ABOUT ENOUGH! *YOU* IS SAYIN' I GOT A *BAD TASTE IN HATS! YOU IS A WALL-EYED OYSTER!*

A INSULT! I CHALLENGE YOU TO A LIFETIME OF BITTER HATRED.

AS THE FIRST STEP IN OUR **LIFETIME FEUD**, I CHALLENGE YOU TO A **CHECKER GAME** WITH COOKIES.

WINNER TAKE *ALL!*

IN AS MUCH AS WE IS PLAYIN' IN **POGO'S** HOUSE WITH **HIS** COOKIES AN' WITHOUT MY GLASSES, *HOUSE RULES* DICTATE THAT YOU GOTTA BE *BLINDFOLDED.*

I CAN BEAT YOU CRAWLIN', BLINDFOLDED, OR SICK ABED.

CAN'T SEE TOO GOOD.... IS YOU PROPER BLINDFOLDED?

NATCHERAL, I IS.....WITH POGO'S NEW EASTER MORN NECKTIE...

AIN'T THAT A BIG, SHINEY, *DIS-*HONEST EYEBALL I SEES POOKIN' OUT......? OR IS *YOU WEARIN' A* SET OF *FRIED EGGS?*

LET'S BE *FAIR....* YOU NEVER SAID WHAT PART GOTTA GIT ALL KIVVERED.

CHAPTER
2

Our Hero Dots One Eye
and Crosses The Other,
Hand Over Hand

18

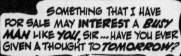

IF YOU IS *SICK* AN' CAN'T SUPPORT YO' *GRAMPA*, YO'*MISSUS*, *NINETEEN CHILLUN*, AN' THE *DOG*.... *THIS POLICY SWINGS INTO ACTION*..

A DOCTOR COMES IN AN' *PATCHES* YOU UP...'FORE YOU KNOWS IT, YOU IS *UP* AN' ON YO'WAY *BACK* TO WORK!

I KNOWED THERE WAS A *CATCH* IN IT!.

YOU GOTTA THINK OF THE *FUTURE*, SIR ...DON'T YOU EVER PLAN FOR A *RAINY DAY*?

NO, I USUAL LETS 'EM COME 'LONG BY THEY SELFS.

YOU IS IMPROVIDENT. HOW CAN YOU TELL WHAT THE DAY AFTER TO-MORROW MAY BE?

IF IT'S ANY-THING EXCEPT *JAN.28*, I IS GONNA WRITE A *NASTY* LETTER TO THE CALENDAR COMPANY.

MY DEAR SIR, *WHY* DO YOU NOT WISH TO PLAN FOR A *RAINY DAY*?

AW, THEY AIN'T NO USE IN *THAT*, SAM... I PLANS ON NOTHIN' BUT THE BEST.....*SUNSHINE* AN' FOUR SQUARE MEALS A DAY....

THE *GUMMINT* NEEDS A MAN LIKE YOU IN THE *RAINY DAY DEP'T*.

I IS GUMMER-MENTAL TIMBER, I ALLUS SAY.

THE S.S. COLIN HAWORTH

21

HEY! COME **BACK!** THE **POLE** STUCK AN' I IS **MAROONED!**

TAKE **CINCINNATI**.... I CAN SELL YOU A FACTORY THERE WHAT CAN PRODUCE **WEATHER** FOR THE *WHOLE DAD BURN U.S.* AND A ---- ANYTHING PEOPLE WANTS: THUNDERSTORMS, *VOLCANO*, HURRICANE, AFTERNOON RAINBOWS, MOON BEAMS *ALL NATIVE BUILT.*

YES, ALBERT, I'LL SELL YOU THE **FACTORY** IN **CINCINNATI** AND YOU CAN START PUTTIN' OUT PATRIOTIC TYPE OF **WEATHER** WITH NO CALL FOR **CANADA** TO *EXPORT* SO MUCH AS A HAILSTONE ....

OL' RICH THORNBURG.

HEY! HELP!

CINCINNATI HAS A YEARLY AVERAGE **TEMPERATURE** OF **53.60°!** BOX THIS AND SELL IT TO PHILADELPHIA IN, SAY, **AUGUST**... AN' ..

HELP!

ROW US HOME, POGO! I IS GONNA BUY THIS BUSINESS!

COME AN' GIT ME! MY POLE GOT STUCK IN THE MUD AN' ME WITH HER....

BY JING! NOT ONLY DID THAT BOY QUIT *POLIN'*.. HE TOOK THE POLE WITH HIM! *EVER'THIN'* GO WRONG UNLESSEN I DO IT MYSELF...

HURRY UP.

OL' RICH THORNBURG

CHAPTER
3

Weather Forecast:
Tiara Boom-De-Ay In
The Afternoon

WHAT IN THE BIG BRIGHT EVER-LOVIN' BLUE-EYED WORLD IS YOU THINKIN' OF?

NOTHIN'.... HONEST.

US IS MERE TAKIN' CARE OF THE LI'L OL' GROUN'CHUCK CHILE...

THAT'S TRUE, ALBERT... THERE IS GRUNDOON, SURE 'NUFF.

MENS, AS US GAZES UPON THIS INNOCENT LI'L' CHILE US GOTTA CORNSIDER THE PERILS AN' PITFALLS WHAT GONNA BE STREWED THRU HIS NATURAL BORN LIFE EVEN AS I AN' YOU.....

PAUSE A MOMENT AN' THINK, FOR INSTINCT, OF THE A-TOMIC, THE B-TOMIC AND THE H-TOMIC BOMB

TIARA

BOOM!

DE AY..?

27

CHAPTER
4

Mole Blooms
In A Spray Of
Myopia

MOTHS! JES' MOTHS! WHERE'S MY $14 BILL?

UGH... WE GOT LOCKED IN.....AN' BEIN' DESPERATE WE *ATE* IT.

ALL? *ALL?* HOW COULD YOU EAT A *WHOLE* $14 BILL.....?

IT WASN'T *EASY.* AT ABOUT HALF PAST ELEVEN DOLLARS WE LOST OUR TASTE FOR MONEY.

BESIDES, WODDY'A WANT? *CHANGE?*

WHAT A *BITTER BLOW!!* THE FAMILY FORTUNE, A *FOURTEEN DOLLAR BILL,* IS *WIPED OUT....* ATEN BY MOTHS....

I GOT MY DOUBTS, ALBERT, OLD FELLOW, IF'N *THAT* TYPE OF CURRENCY IS ANY GOOD ANYWAYS.

YOU GOT DOUBTS? *WE* GOT ULCERS WHAT PROVES IT WAS *NO* GOOD.....US IS MOTHED OUR WAY THRU CORDUROY AN' *PLASTIC* PANTS BUT WE NEVER GUMS NOTHIN' LIKE THAT *CONNERFIT!*

CONNERFIT?! THAT WASN'T CONNERFIT! MY OLD MAMMY MADE THAT BILL HERSELF FROM A SECRET RECIPE SMUGGLED OUT OF THE ROCK HOCKEY ARENA UP ATLANTA WAY....

IT WAS, LET US SAY, *LUMPY.*

TOO MUCH BACON SODA.

OUT! I IS SUFFERED ENOUGH! *I* IS BEEN FLEECED.

FLEECED! TALK LIKE THAT MAKES MY MOUTH WATER.

LET'S HOP A SLOW SHEEP HEADED NORTH.

ALBERT

I IS FEARED I'LL **NEVER** GIT INTO THE WEATHER GAME. MY **FOURTEEN DOLLARS** IS **GONE!**

HOW 'BOUT **TRADING** SOMETHIN', SIR? HOW MUCH IS THAT STUFFED HEAD WORTH?

HIS? I DUNNO AS HE'D **PART** WITH IT... AN' **MEBBE** IT WOULDN'T COME TO **FOURTEEN DOLLARS....**

AN' I **IS** MIGHTY ATTACHED TO IT.

NO! NO! I MEAN THIS HEAD HERE.....IT'S KIND OF **WORED OUT** AN' **FRAZZY** BUT IT JES' MIGHT BRING A **SAWBUCK** OR **TWO....**

HAVE A **CARE,** SIRRAH! STOP BREATHING GERMS AT HONEST MEN.

MOLE!

GOSH, MOLE, WE THOUGHT YOU WERE **DEAD!**

UM..UH..NO.. HEH HEH.

HEH.. AS ANOTHER GREAT HUMORIST ONCE REMARKED: *THAT REMARK IS A GREAT* **EXASPERATION**... HEH.

EXASPER- ATION?

YOU MEAN "EXAGGERATION." AWK!

I KNOW WHAT I MEAN.

I'M NOT *SO* NEAR SIGHTED BUT WHAT I'D OF *NOTICED* IT IN THE MIRROR IF I HAD DIED.

HOW?

YOU'RE JUST IN TIME, MOLE.... OL' SAM IS SELLIN' ALBERT THE *CINCINNATI* POST BUILDIN'... ALBERT'S GONE USE IT FOR A *WEATHER* FACTORY.... TO MAKE GOOD *U.S.* AN' A. TYPE OF WEATHER.

*EX*CELLENT *IDEA*... WE NEED *BETTER* WEATHER THAN CANADA'S BEEN SENDING US .... *THEIR* EXPORT WEATHER IS SHODDY! *SHODDY!*

SLEEZY STUFF IN WINTER... NO *BODY* TO IT.....WEARS THIN IN *NO* TIME....AND THEIR SUMMER STOCK IS LAUGHABLE (*HA HA*)..AN INTERNATIONAL *FRAUD!* TAKE THE GULF STREAM... .....*HAH!*

AIN'T THE GULFSTREAM OUR OWN JOB?

I'D ADVISE YOU TO WASH *YOUR* MOUTH OUT WITH SOAP, DEAR BOY..... *THAT* STREAM IS FROM THE GULF OF *MEXICO! HAH!* ABSOLUTELY UNREGULATED..! WANDERING *WILLY NILLY* ALL OVER OUR SOVEREIGN OCEAN ..... A *SCANDAL!*

JUST ONE QUESTION, MY SON. *WHY* IS ALBERT GOING TO MANUFACTURE WEATHER IN A *FOREIGN* CITY.....? CINCINNATI *INDEED!* WHY GO TO GREECE?

CINCINNATI AIN'T OVER IN GREECE.

DON'T USE *AIN'T*...WHEN I SAY: *IS*...AN' STOP PICKING ON AN'OL' MAN WHAT CAN HARDLY SEE! A CIVIL TONGUE, YOUTH, A *CIVIL* TONGUE!

COULD IT *BE* THAT YOU'RE *AFRAID* TO ANSWER? *PASS THE FISH, LAD....BRISKLY DOES IT.*

HE PICKED CINCINNATI 'CAUSE IT'S THE PLACE WHAT GOT A VERY FINE MEAN TEMPERATURE

MEAN, EH? THAT'S THE *FLIMSY* TYPE WE BEEN GETTING FROM *CANADA*...A CARTEL, NO DOUBT, OF INTERNATIONAL ALLIGATORS...PASS THE BOTTLE OF CHUTNEY, BOY...

US DON'T 'LOW NO DRINKIN' TYPE LICKER IN HERE, MOLE.

NO *CHUTNEY?* ACK! IN THAT CASE, I'LL NEED ANOTHER FISH.....A CRISPY GOLDEN BROWN ONE...

YOU ET 'EM ALL.

A SHAME! YOU DIDN'T EVEN SAVE *ONE* FOR YOUR GOOD COMPANIONS... MR. FOX OR MR. ALLIGATOR? *VERY* THOUGHTLESS, YOUNG MAN.

HEY.

BUT YOU WAS HUNGRY.

NEXT TIME YOU MOVE, SIRRAH, I SHALL CHARGE.

IF CLIFFORD AIN'T YOUR CRAWFISH'S SHO'NUFF NAME, CHURCHY, CALL HIM OFF BY HIS STRAIGHT ONE...

WHEN I CALLS HIM CLIFFORD, IT MAKES HIM BITE STRANGERS. WHEN I CALLS HIM RIGHTLY..... HE BITES ME.

WHAT IN THE WORLD COULD IT BE ..?

WAIT'LL I GIT ON YOUR FAR SIDE --- I'LL WHISPER.... BZZ-MS-SPZ-BZZ..

LAND OF LOVE!

FIERCE... AIN'T IT...?

POOLFSH!

RUN! THE CRITTUR IS OVERHURN US! HERE HE COME!

KIN US HIDE IN HERE WITH YOU? A FIERCE CRAWFISH IS LOOSE.

A CRAWFISH? EIGHT FEET TALL? BREATHES FIRE AN' ROARS?

NO-- HE'S 'BOUT'S BIG'S A SAN'WINCH. BREATHES SWAMP WATER, QUIETLIKE.

HE'S RARIN' 'CAUSE 'STEAD OF CALLIN' HIM CLIFFORD, I CALLS HIM BY HIS RIGHT NAME.

FOOF WHAT'S WRONG WITH THAT ?

35

ALL RIGHT, SAM. *THERE'S* THE SHILLIN'...... THE *MEXICAN SHILLIN'*...

AN' NOW YOU ARE *SOLE* POSSESSOR OF MY INTEREST IN THE CINCINNATI POST BUILDING.

I'LL GIVE THE COIN A *TEST*...... *AOUGH!* IT TASTES *TERRIBLE*...

HAW! NOTHIN' BUT A *COUGH-DROP!* MINTAGE OF 1927.. ... *I FOXED YOU OUTEN YO' INTEREST!*)

HA! WAIT'LL YOU PUT THE BITE ON THE POST!

1 NEVER HAD NO INTEREST IN THAT BUILDING *ANY-WAYS*.... PREFERRED A THEATRE DOWN THE STREET-- SO *THERE!*

YOU OWES ME A UNGUMMED COUGHDROP.

LOST MY EYEGLASSES IN A BITTER BATTLE WITH A *CRUSTACEAN!* A CRAWFISH YCLEPT *CLIFFORD.*

LOOKIN' FOR 'EM, HUH?

YAWP!

I FOUND 'EM! BENT IN THE FRACAS, NO DOUBT.... BUT STILL CLEAR AS A CRYSTAL.... 20·20

UH... YOU IS MORE FOUND CLIFFORD, MR. MOLE...

DON'T SEE HOW YOU CAN SEE THRU HIM, DIRTY AS HE IS.

HE IS A TRIFLE TIGHT, TOO...

WHO DOES EITHER OF YOU KNOW IN CINCINNATI? FELLA IS SENT YOU A PACKAGE AN' A HANDWROT LETTER.

IT'S FROM A EDITOR GO BY NAME OL' DICK THORNBURG....IT SAY: DEAR HONORABLE SIRS: PLEASE ACCEPT THESE TOKENS OF OUR ESTEEM. YRS TRULY ETC.

A KEY... LABELED KEY TO THE CITY ----- MMM-- KEY TO THE CITY OF FORT MUDGE?

RIGHT NEXT DOOR.

YRS TRULY ETC. ? WHO'S I KNOW NAME OF ETC.?

AN' A FRAMED MOTTO: "THERE AIN'T NO EVER- LOVIN' BLUE EYED PLACE LIKE HOME."

YOU THINK HE'S IM- PLYIN' ANY- THING?

HE MUSTN'T OF KNOW HOW TO SPELL HIS NAME! PHOO. ON ETC.

CHAPTER
5

Wherein Our Hero Learns
That Hospitality Is
Merely Mortal

41

42

HOW'D YOU LIKE TO BE A GREAT CLOWN? *Outward all laughs?*

BUT INWARD DYIN' OF A *BROKING HEART?* HOT DOG!

RIGHT! EVERYBODY WOULD LAUGH *BUT* → INSIDE ← you is all TRAGEDY ☆ (a little SOFT MUSIC, SOUSA)

HOW 'BOUT TAGGER RIG?

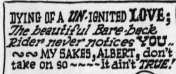

DYING OF A *UN*-IGNITED LOVE; *The beautiful Bare-back Rider never notices YOU* ~~ MY SAKES, ALBERT, don't take on so ~~~-it ain't *TRUE!*

YOWP! YOWP!

AW, I WASN'T TAKIN' ON --- I WAS HOLLER'N' 'CAUSE OL' CUMQUOTH HERE WAS HITTIN' *ME* 'STEAD OF THE DRUM --- UH---WHAT'S THIS JOB LIKELY TO PAY?

PIERROT OL' BOY, US THOUGHT YOU WAS BEIN' THIS CLOWN FOR *LAUGHS.*

ALBERT, my boy, A CAREER of FAME-STUDDED *Stardom* awaits → *YOU* ☆ ~~~ YOUR PLACE *is on the* TANBARK *with the* pleasaunt *cry of* "HEY RUBE" WAFTED ON THE SUMMER AIR!!!!

WELL, C'MON IN AN' SET A SPELL ---- I IS EXPECTIN' *POGO* --- HE'LL HELP ME DECIDE. *MEANWHILES US'LL SNACK A BIT.*

IF'N I GOES OFF WITH THE *CIRCUS* WHAT'LL POOR POGO DO WITHOUT ME? I SORTA LOOKS AFTER HIM.

Why, *YOU* are . the ➡️*SOUL*⬅️ of GENEROSITY, ☆ ☆ALLOW THE *poor waif* to lodge here in *YOUR* *ABSENCE!!*

SURE.... ALL THIS STUFF YOU'RE GIVIN' *US* COULD BE HIS....YOU SEEM TO GOT PLENTY.

IT'S ALREADY HIS. THIS HERE IS *POGO'S* PLACE ...

OOP, S'CUSE ME ... DIN'T MEAN TO BLUNDER INTO NO *RESTAURANT.*

C'MON IN, POGO, YOU IS WELCOME. HAPPEN THIS IS *YOUR* PLACE.

SON, US IS CELEBRATIN'A *BIG* OPPORTUNITY! *FAME* AND *FORTUNE!* THE *NAME* IN LIGHTS .....*TALENT IN FULL FLOWER!*

Gay CIRCUS LIFE *BECKONS!!* *The APPLAUSE of Thousands!* LAUGHTER! *Song!* Cheers *on every* ➡️Hand⬅️ *!!* DOES THAT SOUND *Acceptable,* SIR?

GOSH, I DUNNO, I'M OVERCOME... I·UH··WELL, YES.

FINE! *THAT'S ALL, POGO!* I ACCEPTS, P.T., GET OUT THE CONTRACK AN', POGO, PUT ON MORE COFFEE AN' SEE KIN YOU BAKE UP A CAKE.

CHAPTER
6

Brains From Far And Wide
Are Summoned To Ponder
A Suicide Pack

PLOCK!

A BOOBY TRAP! IF I DIN'T OF SEED IT MYSELF I WOULD OF THUNK I COULDN'TNA B'LEEVE HE WOULDA OF DOOD IT HIS-SELF 'LESS I SAWN HE REAL MUS' OF DID DO IT WITH MY OWN EYES.....

WITH THIS *GARBAGE* HANGIN' OUTEN MY BAG, FOLKS'LL THINK I DON'T KNOW HOW TO *PACK!* ---- I'LL GO BACK IN AN' *CLIP* OFF THE *HANGOVERS.*

OW! DAG NAG THAT *POGO*.... I FERGOT 'BOUT HIM HAVIN' THAT *MISSIN' DOORSTEP!*

OR ...UM, LET'S SEE ... I FERGOT 'BOUT HIM *NOT* HAVIN' A MISSIN' DOOR-STEP...

STILL HOW COULD HE *NOT* HAVE IT IF HE *DO* BUT HOW COULD HE *DO* IF ...*YAWK!*

BY JING! HE DOGBONE WELL BETTER *GIT IT FIXED!* GOT IT OR NOT!

I ASK **CLIPPED** QUESTIONS, SIR---- IF THE DOG'S GONE HE'S MISSIN' OR DEAD? WHO? WHICH?

I DUNNO! *EVER'BODY* WAS **NUTS** ABOUT HIM.

THE CASE IS BLOCKED! *"EVER'BODY WAS NUTS!"* THAT PART OF THE REPORT MAKES ME THINK! AS A **COP** I'M THROWIN' EVERY BRAIN IN MY HEAD INTO THIS.

AS LONG AS WE'RE **SHORT HANDED** I'LL GO GET **HELP!**

HEY, HOUN'DOG, C'MON AN' *HELP!* SOMETHIN' MUST IS HAPPENED TO *PUP DOG.* I LEFT HIM TIED UP... COULD YOU SNIFF OUT THE TRAIL?

GLADLY AN' IN DUTI-BALLY.

ALBERT STOPS BY..SEES I LEFT OL' PUP TIED TO THE DOOR STEP----ALBERT PICKS UP A SUITCASE... *PFFFT!* THE PUP IS **GONE!**

HAS OL' ALBERT STILL GOT THE GRIP?

NO, JUS' A LI'L COUGH--- HE FEEL JUS' FINE.

NO MORE OF THAT! THAT IS, IF YOU WANTS MY KEEN NOSE ON THE JOB... STUFFED THO' IT IS WITH *PNEUMONIA.*

YOU DON'T SMELL AS GOOD AS YOU DID?

GROWL.

CHAPTER
7

The Case Is Open
And/Or Shut At Will

YOU KNOW THE *FIRST THING* WE OUGHT TO FIND OUT 'BOUT THE MISSIN' PUP DOG?

SURE, WHERE IS HE.

WHAT KIND OF SLOPPY PO-LICE WORK IS *THAT? YOU'RE GOIN'* AT IT *ALL BACKWARDS.'*

BACK-WARDS? AIN'T WE S'POSED TO FIND OUT WHERE IS HE?

FINDIN' *THAT* OUT COMES *LAST!* WHEN WE DO THAT THE CASE IS *DONE. NOW, WHAT* COMES AHEAD OF *THAT?*

ACTUAL, **WHO** STOLT HIM?

NOT SO FAST! FIRST, (TIME 11:17) WE FIGGER OUT *WHO* WE SUSPECKS. YOU GOTTA PROCEED SCIENTIFIC!

THIS HERE MYSTERY WAS A LOT SIMPLER WHEN IT ONLY HAD ME THINKIN' ABOUT IT.

BRains, Size 6¼, Are
Pooled To Form A Shallow
But Slippery Puddle

58

WELL, *TIME 1:00!* I'LL REOPEN THE CASE... NOW, WHO DO YOU SUSPECT, OWL?

OL' MOLE! *THAT'S WHO!*

MOLE?

YESSIR, *HIM!* YOU NOTICE HIM SNOOPIN' AROUN'? *OH*, HE GOT A *BAD* NAME.... *HE* AIN'T UP TO *NO* GOOD... AN' *WHAT'S MORE*....

I SAID TO HIM: "*SEED THE PUP DOG?*" "I SAYS... AN' *HE* SAYS: "*WHO?*"... *HA!* WHO INDEED!.. *HE* DODGED! AN' ALL THE TIME HE GOT THAT *SNEAKY LOOK* IN HIS EYE.

WHICH EYE WAS THIS HERE *SNEAKY LOOK IN*, SIR?

ALL OF 'EM!

IN ROUND NUMBERS HOW MANY WOULD YOU SAY? AT A *ROUGH GUESS?*

MAN! I IS *WORED OUT!* TROMPIN' ALL OVER THE SWAMP AN' NARY *HIDE NOR HAIR* OF THE PUP.

HEY! IS YOU SEED ANYTHIN' OF OL' *MOLE* WHILE YOU WAS OUT LOOKIN' FOR THE *PUP DOG?*

NOPE! WE DIN'T SEE THE PUP AN' WE DIN'T SEE *MOLE*, NEITHER.

ADD THAT UP, PARDNER. **TIME 1:12**...Remarks: *Both the Mole and the Pup wasn't seen*

IN OTHER WORDS: TOGETHER, THEY IS **MISSIN'!**

CHECK! AN' YOU CAN ADD, (TIME 1:13½) *The Mole ain't talkin'*

THE WAY **EVIDENCE** IS PILIN' UP, *IT IS POSITIVELY UNCANNY!*

IT'S SURE TOO DEEP FOR ME.... I NEED MY BOOTS.

I THINK ALBERT AN' BEAUREGARD ARE ON THE **RIGHT TRAIL** ....IT LOOKS LIKE OL' MOLE DID IT ALLRIGHT.

DID WHAT?

SNATCHED THE **PUP DOG** OF COURSE..... HE'S PROB'LY A UNDERCOVER DOG CATCHER.

YOU AN' ALBERT AN' THE HOUN' DOG SURE BEEN **TALKIN'!**

YES, INDEED! WE'VE DISCUSSED, RE-CUSSED.... ALL WAS GIVE A FAIR CHANCE TO TALK AN' DEE-FEND MOLE...BUT WE ENDED UP SUSPECTIN' HIM FAIR AN' SQUARE....

DID YOU HAVE TIME TO THINK?

ALL IN GOOD TIME....WE AIN'T THE SLOPPY KIND WHAT TRIES TO DO **TWO** THINGS AT ONCE. UP TO **NOW** WE BEEN JES' **TALKIN'**...BUT WHEN WE START **THINKIN'** 'BOUT THIS-- **STAND BACK!**

JES' SO YOU DON'T FERGIT IT.

62

SOMEBODY'S LOOKIN' AT OUR PIT FALL·· I'LL RUSH AROUN' ONE WAY···

AN' I'LL RUSH 'ROUN' T'OTHER···

··· AN' WE'LL COTCH HIM ATWIXT OF····

·····US.

WE GOT THIS MOLE FOOLED···HE THINKS WE GRABBED EACH OTHER ON PURPOSE, HA!

YEAH···SHHH·· LET'S SPRING ON HIM···PULL HIS COAT OVER HIS HEAD IN A DAZZLIN' DISPLAY OF JIMINY JITSU!

INTO THE BUSH!

63

GOT HIM! BUNDLE HIS HEAD IN HIS COAT!

YESSIR! GOT HIM! DAGNAB, LOOKY, HOUN'DOG! AIN'T OL' MOLE'S UNDER-PINNIN' A RIDICULOUS SIGHT?!

EVER'THIN' ALL RIGHT?

UH----OH, HULLO UNCLE BALDWIN! I GOT OL' MOLE HERE ---CAUGHT HIM RED HANDED---WHERE'S HOUN' DOG?

NO MATTER! HE RUN OUT! WE'LL FORCE A CONFESSION OUTEN MOLE.

GRAB THAT STICK! EVER'BODY TAKE TURNS WHACKIN' 'TIL MOLE TELLS US WHERE PUP DOG IS!

BUT, ALBERT, YOU DON'T KNOW IF MOLE TOOK PUP DOG.

DON'T GIMME THAT! MOLE LOOKS GUILTY ENOUGH TO HANG--- GO AHEAD!

GUILTY OF WHAT, PRAY TELL?

YEAH, *O*-KAY, MOLE..... YOU'LL GIT YOUR TURN TO WHACK MOLE AN' MAKE MOLE TELL WHERE HE HID PUPDOG. SO JES' GIT IN LINE, MOLE, AN'...

MOLE!?

UM.

DOG BONE! YOU IS MOLE! THEN WHO'S I GOT *HERE?*

WHO, INDEED?

AN' *WHY*, TOO?

BLESS MY SOFT BROWN EYES ..... *IT'S BEAU-REE-GARD!*

TO *THINK* THAT *YOU*, MY FELLOW-SLEUTH, IS THE KIDNAPPER --

WHAT?

ALBERT! YOU SUSPECTS ONE MAN, CATCHES THE *WRONG* ONE AN' SO YOU CLAIMS THE ONE YOU *IS GOT* IS *GUILTY!* JUS' CATCHIN' A MAN DON'T PROVE HE'S A *CULPRIT!*

IT'S A GOOD *START*.. AIN'T IT?

A VERY GOOD START.

'LONG AS YOU TURNS OUT NOT TO BE MOLE, I GUESS WE DON'T WHACK NOBODY.

YEAH.... HOUN'DOG YOU IS A SPOIL-SPORT.

IT'S A GOOD THING I PACKED SOME OF YOUR GRUB IN YOUR BAG WITH YOUR TRAVELIN' CLO'ES FOR ME, POGO, 'CAUSE I IS WORKED UP A APPETITE....

QUITE SO.

JUS' THE SAME, MOLE, IF I HAD MY WAY, WE'D SHAKE A CONFESSION OUTEN YOU! ---I STILL THINK YOU STOLE THAT POOR LI'L--

-- PUP DOG.

DID YOU PUT ANY LIVERWITCH IN---?

YOU PACKED LUNCH RIGHT IN WITH SOCKS AN' ALL?

LOOK! ALBERT, YOU PACKED THE PUP DOG INTO THE SUITCASE --- THAT'S WHERE HE IS BEEN ALL THIS TIME!

AN' I 'THUNK HE WAS AT DEATH'S DOOR --- AW, THAT DEAR LI'L FELLA, I WOULDN'T WANT ANYTHIN' TO HAPPEN TO HIM!

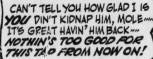

CAN'T TELL YOU HOW GLAD I IS *YOU* DIN'T KIDNAP HIM, MOLE---- IT'S GREAT HAVIN' HIM BACK--- NOTHIN'S TOO GOOD FOR THIS TAD FROM NOW ON!

HOWEVER--- *WHAT NO GOOD LI'L' BUG ET ALL THE LUNCH WHAT I PACKED IN WITH YOU, PUP?*

US MIGHT'S WELL ALL GO TO MY PLACE AN' CELEBRATE FINDIN' *PUP DOG* WITH A LI'L' PARTY.

AIN'T YOU SHAMED? YOU OWES **MOLE** A APOLOGY. *YOU* PACKED PUP DOG IN BY MISTAKE **AND** YOU WAS SAYIN' **MOLE** WAS A **KIDNAPPER** ... WANTED HIM *LYNCHED*

BUT I WAS LOOKIN' FOR S'PICIOUS CRITTURS .....VARMINTS WHAT COULD DO A *DIRTY TRICK* LIKE THAT! AN' 'LONG COME THAT *SNEAKY MOLE*, A OLD ENEMY---

BUT *YOU* WAS GUILTY---AN' YOU BLAMED HIM *UNFAIR!* ENEMY OR NOT.

WHAT DOG BONED GOOD IS A ENEMY IF YOU CAN'T BLAME HIM FOR STUFF LIKE THAT THERE! !?

CHAPTER
9

A Medium Rare Day
In June Is Well Done

IT'S A JUMPY WAY OF LIFE, ANYWAYS.

I BEEN FIGGERIN' OUT WHAT YOU SAID---- THAT WE AIN'T GOT NO *FIFTY FIRST* OF OCTOBER.

WHAT'S TO FIGGER OUT 'BOUT *THAT?*

ALL THE *FIFTY FIRSTS* OF *OCTOBERS* FALL ON THE *TWENTEETHS* OF NOVEMBERS.

OCTOBER STOP ON THE THIRTY ONE OF IT.

WHY?

YOU CAN'T GO HAVIN' A WHOLE *YEARFUL* OF OCTOBER.

WHY NOT...? IT'S A *PERTY* MONTH .... WE COULD HAVE OCTOBER, CHRISTMAS, THE FOURTH OF JULY AN' MY BIRTHDAY AN' LET ALL THE OTHER MONTHS GO .... *FEBRUARY FOR INSTINCT... WHO* NEEDS IT?

JANUARY NEEDS IT--- KEEPS IT FROM BUNKIN' INTO MARCH!

COME COME -- LET US BE REALISTIC.

I THINK I GOT THE **NEW CALENDAR** *ALL* SET.

NEW CALENDAR?

YEP... THE *OCTOBER CALENDAR*... CHRISTMAS COMES ON THE **86**TH OF OCTOBER.

ONE GOOD MONTH ALL YEAR LONG. THE **FIRST** OF THE YEAR FALLS ON OCTOBER NINETY-THIRD....WODDY YOU THINK OF THAT!

OH, I DUNNO.....IT'S ONE OF THEM THINGS I DON'T THINK ABOUT VERY MUCH.

CHAPTER
10

A Friend Is Drunk
On A Sobering Note

IF YOU IS A *PERFESSIONAL* PREE-DICTER WHERE'D YOU PREEDICK AT AFORE?

I WORKED FOR A *NEW ORLEANS* NEWSPAPER.

I WAS THE ORIGINAL *PICAYUNE FROG*.. A WEATHER EXPERT... BUT THE BOSS, HONEST GEORGE, WAS A *HARD MAN*... MADE ME WEAR SHOES... SAID I WAS SOGGY AN' HE DIN'T LIKE HIS CARPETS ALL DAMPED.... *THIS*, OF COURSE, MADE MY FEET HURT .....

NATURAL, I PREDICKS *RAIN* FOR *SIXTY SEVEN DAYS*... OL' GEORGE SAT AT HIS DESK UNDER A *UMBRELLA* AN' CARRIED A LOADED LIGHTNIN' ROD AT ALL TIMES .... *WELL*, SIR! WE HAD SIXTY SEVEN DAYS OF *UN*-MITIGATED SUNSHINE ....

HONEST GEORGE PEEKS OUT AN' HE *SEE* : SOMETHIN' *IS WRONG.* HE TOOK BACK THE COMP'NY SHOES, GUV *ME* THE SACK AN' BRUNG IN ANOTHER BOY.... *WHO KNOWS, MEBBE A RELATIVE* ... BUT ANYWAY A IMPOSTOR WHO COULDN'T PREDICK *X*MAS ON DEC. 24.

THAT IS OCTOBER 457th.

THIS NEW ORLEANS PAPER HELD A CONTEST TO SEE WHO'D BE THE WEATHER MAN... *ME* OR A OUTLANDER NAMED *"POGO"* (SAID TO HAVE SHARP WEATHER EARS.)

HA! ME AN' OL' GEORGE, THE HEAD MAN, FIXED *THAT!* WE BOLSTERED THE BALLOT BOX AN' I WAS A *SHOO IN!* ..... *ONLY LATER* DID I LEARN THAT THE JOB CARRIED *NO* SALARY.

74

I DENOUNCED THIS PENURIOUS ATTITUDE AND FOUND MYSELF AT *LIBERTY*...SO I PICKETED THE MARDI GRAS SINGLEHANDED... *GEORGE* CHARGED THAT I WAS NOT A *FROG* BUT A MIDGET *ALLIGATOR!* A VILE SLANDER!

ON *WHO*, HOPPY TOES?

WHAT'S IN THE SATCHEL, YOU *SHORT* TAILED SALAMAGANDER?

I WOULDN'T TELL ANY OVERGROWED LIZARD...

NOTHIN' BUT WATER...

I COME OVER TO SET UP A FORECASTIN' BUREAU.....

HAW.... I'LL JES' DRINK IT UP... I'LL LEARN HIM TO BE SO SMART.

I GOT A AMOEBA IN WATER... HE KNOWS *EVER'THIN'*

HE FORECASTS WEATHER AN' ...*HEY! YOU POT-EYED PLATTER-PUSS!* YOU DRUNK MY *FRIEND!*

CHAPTER
11

Owl Goes
Slumming

"I *KNOW* YOU IS A *BUSY MAN*, MR. PICAYUNE HOP FROG, BUT *HOW* COME YO' A-MOEBA HAS *H-2-O* ON HIS LI'L' SATCHEL?"

"IT'S HIS 'NITIALS."

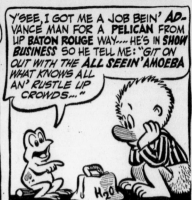

"Y'SEE, I GOT ME A JOB BEIN' AD-VANCE MAN FOR A *PELICAN* FROM UP *BATON ROUGE* WAY.... HE'S IN *SHOW BUSINESS* SO HE TELL ME: "GIT ON OUT WITH THE *ALL SEEIN'* AMOEBA WHAT KNOWS ALL AN' RUSTLE UP CROWDS...""

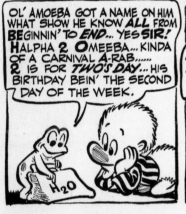

"OL' AMOEBA GOT A NAME ON HIM WHAT SHOW HE KNOW *ALL* FROM *BEGINNIN'* TO *END*... YES *SIR!* HALPHA 2 OMEEBA... KINDA OF A CARNIVAL A-RAB...... 2 IS FOR *TWO'S DAY*... HIS BIRTHDAY BEIN' THE SECOND DAY OF THE WEEK."

"THOUGHT *TUESDAY* WAS THE *THIRD* DAY OF THE WEEK."

"*NO*, YOU'RE THINKIN' OF *THIRD'S DAY*...COMES AFORE FRIDAY.....*DON'T FEEL BAD, THO*,' 'TAIN'T NO DISGRACE TO BE STUPID."

"WHAT'S THE STORY 'BOUT THIS PELICAN?"

"MUS' OF IS START *WAY* BACK. MAN, GO BY NAME OF *NAPOLEUM*, HE COME 'LONG AN' HE SAY TO TH' *PELICAN*, HE SAY, "*BOY*, HOW YOU LIKE TO BUY *LOU'SIANA*?""

"HEE! HE MUS' OF TOLE NAPOLEUM "GO BACK THAT FLITTER-FLY HOUSE." *HE* COULDN'T OF BOUGHT LOUISIANA."

"*HE DID TOO BOUGHT IT*,' INCLUDIN' *NORTH* AN' *SOUTH DA-KOTA!*"

CHAPTER
12

An Affair Of Honor
Is An
Inside Job

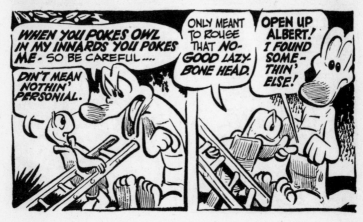

WHAT? WHAT!?

A WATER PISTOL.

THEY ISN'T GOT YO' AMOEBA OUT 'TIL YET!

I REPEATS, TURTLE, IF YOU AN' ALBERT HAD *ANY* BRAINS WE WOULDN'T *BE* IN THIS MESS.

IF YOU IS TRYIN' TO INSULT *ALBERT*, C'MON OUT AN' *FIGHT* HIM!

I'M *STUCK* AN' BESIDES I KIN INSULT HIM FROM HERE

I (ON ALBERT'S BEHALF) RESENT YO' IMPERTIMENTS.... CHOOSE YO' WEAPONS .... I CHALLENGE YOU (ON ALBERT'S BEHALF)

I CHOOSES BOMBS, GUNS, AN' DAGGERS! EN GARDE!

YOU CAN'T SCARE ALBERT! (I ACCEPTS ON ALBERT'S BEHALF, AGIN.)

85

FIRST OF ALL, THO', I'LL GRAB UP A SWORD FROM MY AMMUNITION DUMP (FOR WORK IN **CLOSE QUARTERS**), BECAUSE, *VERY LIKELY*, TURTLE---

--- WILL **HACK** HIS WAY **IN** AFTER ME AN' WE'LL HAVE A ***WILD FREE-SWINGIN' SWORD FIGHT UP** AN' **DOWN** STAIRS!*

SLUM THAT **SAM'WICH** DOWN IN **BACK** OF OWL 'CAUSE HIS **FRONT** IS *TICKLISH*---- HOPE YOU PUT PLENTY ---UH-UH-----

YEH..... I PUT *PLENTY*----

UH-UH

--- PEPPER ON IT

The Hose Is Carried
To Extremes

89

I'D RUTHER BE BURNED UP THAN FISHED UP.

WITH MY METHODS YOU CAN HAVE BOTH --- NOW THEN, THE FISH ---

HERE'S THE *LAST* OF THE *FISH* YOU FLUNG.

WAIT 'TIL I *TALLY* 'EM UP.

I CARRY THE HOSE.

WHAT'S YOU GOTTA *TALLY* UP? THEY WAS ONLY *THREE.*

NOW! NOW! YOU IS GIVE ME *TWO* ... THIS ONE MAKES *THREE.*

HOLD HIM A MINUTE .... WHERE'S THE OTHER TWO --- AH, HERE --- WELL, *THAT ONE IS THREE* -- SO THIS ONE IS *FOUR* ... THIS ONE IS *FIVE* ...

SIX.

I CARRY THE HOSE.

SEE! SIX! IT PAYS TO TALLY UP, HOUN' DOG ... DON'T IT NOW?

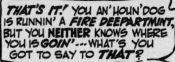

In Which It Is Seen
That It Is Hard To Hold
As Much As A Pelican

PHOO--ALL IS LOST.

LOST MY AMOEBA WITH THE GOLD TOOTH --- LOST MY SATCHEL AN'---

AN'-.

AN' LOST YO' JOB, PICAYUNE! A FINE ADVANCE MAN YOU IS BEEN FOR ME!

ROOGEY BATOON! THE UNDENIABLE PELICAN! THE MAN WHO MADE THE LOU'SIANA PURCHASE...

HOW'D YOU DO IN THAT CALAVERAS COUNTY JUMP, CHAMP?

THEY THREW A RINGER AT ME.... A NON-GUILD MEMBER... HARDLY A FROG A-TALL!

I HAPPEN TO KNOW IT WAS A SMALL SALT-LAKE CITY GRASS-HOPPER... HE HOPPED YOU BLIND!

HE USED WINGS! HE USED WINGS!

SO DO YOU... IN THE BAYOU! WATER WINGS!

HEY DOWN THERE!

IF ONLY WE HAD SOMETHIN TO DROP TO SNARE THEIR ATTENTION.

GREAT IDEA, PICAYUNE.

THEM MYSTERIFUL VOICES FROM OUTEN NOWHERES.

BLOWNK

DID YOU HEAR A SORT OF A HOLLOW SOUND?

HEY! ALBERT!

SOMETHIN' IS STRUCK ME, POGO----- LET'S BEAT IT!

LET'S.

GOOD! WE IS EXCAPIN' SO FAST I IS ALMOST LOSIN' MY HAT!

HOT DOG!

HAT? *I* AIN'T GOT NO HAT.

HEY!

THEY IS COME FOR US, POGO.

POGO, TELL ALBERT WE AIN'T *SUPER-NATURAL*

LOOKIN' AT YO' FRIEND I B'LEEVE THAT IS HARD TO B'LEEVE.

DIN'T YOU IS *EVER* SEE A PELICAN AFORE?

SURE, FOLKS, THIS HERE IS GOOD OL' *ROOGEY BATOON*, THE LOU'SIANA TYPE PELICAN.

HE'S THE BOY WHAT MADE THE *LOU'SIANA PURCHASE.*

MY! IS YOU REALLY ?

YUP.

YUP.... I MADE ALL *THREE* OF 'EM.

HUH?

HUH?

HUH?

96

CHAPTER
15

A Bass Baritoon,
A Contraltor And
A Treble Cleft Palate

IT *MOUGHT* BE OF INTEREST TO YOU TO KNOW THERE IS THEM AS DOUBTS YOU MADE THE **LOU'SIANA** PURCHASE.

PICAYUNE, YOU **KNOWS'** I MADE 'EM... *ALL* AND *EVERY THREE* OF 'EM!

ALL **THREE** OF 'EM ? *WHAT'S YOU* **MEAN**? *JES' WHAT DOES YOU THINK THE LOU'SIANA PURCHASE* IS ANYWAYS **?!**

FISH! FISH THEY IS.... *NATURAL THEY IS FISH...AN'* I MADE ALL *THREE.... LEARNED 'EM! GROOMED 'EM!*

FISH... *FISH?*

FLIM, FLAM AND *FLO'*... THE *LOU'SIANA PERCHES!* A STELLAR SET OF SQUAMOSE SONGSTERS.

NO ... IT CAN'T BE.. .....THE LOU'SIANA PERCHES ---- **?**?

I TOLE POGO HERE 'BOUT YOU HAD A SINGIN' TRIO ....*FLIM*, *FLAM* AN' *FLO* ....

YEP, THE *THREE* LOU'SIANA PERCHES.

A BASS BARITOON... A *CONTRALTOR,* AN' A TREBLE CLEFT PALATE.

FLIM, FLAM AN' AN' FLO'...SIMPLY SPLENDIFEROUS STELLAR STARRED *SQUAMOSE* SONGSTERS. STICK YO' HEAD IN, FRIEND.

DID YOU *HEAR 'EM?* SONGBIRDS OF THE DEPTHS PRACTICIN' A NEW *ROUSER*... "ASLOOP IN THE DOOP."...LIKE IT?

GLOOP.

TRYIN' TO LISTEN TO YO' SONGFISHES UNDER THE WATER IS *RISKY* AN' *SOGGY.*

HOW RISKY?

LEAVIN' MY *EARS* OPEN THAT WAY, I IS LIKELY TO GIT WATER ON THE *BRAIN.*

WELL, YO' TURTLE FRIEND CAN'T GIT WATER ON NO BRAIN.

SEE HOW YOU LIKES THE **LOU'SIANA PERCHES** SINGIN' "A SLOOP IN THE DOOP."

SOUNDS KINDA *GURGLY*...SOMETHIN' IS THROWIN' 'EM OFF---I THINK ONE OF 'EM GOT A *FROG* IN HER THROAT.

SIR!

IF ONE OF THE SINGIN' **LOU'SIANA PERCHES** IS GOT A BAD THROAT IT'S FROM OVER-WORK---THEY NEEDS A REST.

THEY NEEDS A LITTLE **VACATION**---A CULTURAL TRIP TO **DR. BRENNAN'S UPSTAIRS WAXWORKS** --- OR A EDUCATIONAL TOUR OF THE **VIEUX CARRÉ.**

YOU FERGITS WE ISN'T IN N'ORLEANS.

RIGHT, PICAYUNE -- MEBBE YOU GENTS COULD SUGGEST A *GENTEEL* DIVERSION FOR THREE MAIDEN PERCHES?

THINK THEY'D LIKE TO GO **FISH!N'**, POGO?

SHUSH, THEY *IS* FISH.

WULL---I GOT A CAN OF **BAIT** OVER'T MY PLACE. FIGGER THEY'D LIKE TO HELP **UNSNARL** A FEW YARDS OF **NIGHT CRAWLERS**?

IT'S QUIET BUT ABSORBIN' WORK.

101

THEM **DAMES** ISN'T SHOWNED UP...

WE'S S'POSE TO MEET 'EM HERE.

THEY GONE BE LATE FOR **DINNER**.

WIMMEN IS QUEER CRITTURS-'MEMBER THE ONE WHAT **AD**VERTISED FOR A HUSBAN' CLAIMIN' SHE WAS A **RICH WIDDER** --- AN' WANTED TO MARRY A **HAN'SOME MAN** OF *BREEDIN'* AN' *CULTURE* AND *GREAT WEALTH!*

AN' YOU SENT IN **MY** PICTURE WHICH NATURAL *HYPNOTISED* HER.

AN' WHEN SHE SHOWED UP--SHE WASN'T **RICH** AT ALL--

SHE WAS A **SPIDER!** A BLACK WIDOW SPIDER.

AAAH-WHAT **DU**PLICITY!

WONDER WHAT HAPPENED TO THE **GIRLS**?

THE BATS WAS S'POSE TO MEET **FLIM, FLAM** AN' **FLO** RIGHT OVER THERE.

MIGHTY NICE OF 'EM TO TAKE THE GIRLS OUT.

HERE COMES **POGO** AN' THE PELICUM WHAT CLAIM HE **MADE** THEM GAL SINGERS INTO A **SUCCESS.**

BUT WHERE IS THE YOUNG LADIES?

105

CHAPTER
16

The Bite
Of The
Remedy

107

108

FRIEND, *YOU* LOOK LIKE AN *HONEST* MAN... WOULD YOU RESPECT *ANY* MAN WHO SOLD YOU SOMETHIN' YOU DIDN'T *NEED?*

'COURSE NOT.

SNAKE

RIGHT! AND *SO,* FRIEND, I GO TO THE TROUBLE AN' *EXPENSE* OF GIVIN' YOU A *FREE* SNAKE BITE *BEFORE I SELL YOU A SINGLE DROP OF REMEDY!*

WHAT'S WRONG WITH *THAT?*

I'LL THINK OF SOMETHIN'

AS A SPECIAL INTRODUCIAL OFFER, I'M GONNA SELL YOU *TWO* BOTTLES FOR THE PRICE OF *ONE.*

NO, YOU'RE NOT..... I DON'T NEED *NO* SNAKE-BITE CURE.

GO AHEAD AN' *SNAP 'EM UP,* POGO ----- IT'S A *BIG BARGAIN* ..... *A THING LIKE THIS DON'T COME ALONG EVERY DAY* ....

THANK GOODNESS! I REPEATS: I DON'T GOT *NO* SNAKE-BITES.

I'LL THROW IN A *FREE* SNAKE-BITE. C'MERE, S'NAVELY.

GO AHEAD -- *THINK HOW HE'LL FEEL IF YOU REFUSES.*

THINK HOW *I'LL* FEEL IF THAT SNAKE *BITES* ME.

SNAKES

DOGGONE, SNAVELY! IS YOU BEEN AT THE *REMEDY* AGAIN?

HOTCHA! I BIT MYSELF, BOSS... IT WAS A CASE OF LIFE OR *WORSE.*

SNAKE!

C'MON, SNAVELY...THERE'S A CUSTOMER OUT HERE. HE WANTS YOU TO PUT THE *BITE* ON HIM.

I DO NOT!

S'ALL RIGHT, FRIEND... *I* AIN'T HONGRY NO WAYS. *HAPPY* NEW YEAR AN' NO HARD FEELIN'S.

I GOT A FEELIN', SNAVELY, THAT YOU IS CONSUMED *ALL* THE SNAKE-BITE REMEDY. I'LL RULE YOU OFF THE TURF FOR *LIFE*.... WHERE'S YOUR *ASSISTANT?*

THE APPRENTICE COBRA? HE'S LEARNIN' TO RATTLE.

IS *THIS* THE BOY YOU HIRED? HE'S NOTHIN' BUT A *ANGLE-WORM!* WHERE'S HIS *TEETH?*

ON THE END *YOU'RE* LOOKIN' AT, CHIEF, MIGHTY MIGHTY *FEW* OF US GOT TEETH.

GREAT NEWS! I'VE SECURED TWO LOWERS ON A *FREIGHT* LEAVIN' FOR *BATON ROUGE!*

JES' ABOUT IN TIME TOO... I IS BEEN *SORE TRIED* LATELY.

ME AN' THE *APPRENTICE COBRA* HERE WILL STICK A-ROUND.... I'M NOT BEIN' CHASED BY *NO* RAILWAY *POL*ICE AGAIN.

NATURAL, *YOU'LL* WANT TO **THANK** ME, AFORE I LEAVES FER GIVIN' YOU A **START** OUT HERE, WON'T YOU?

NO, BUT I'LL GIVE YOU A START *BACK.* JES' BEND OVER AN' I'LL.....

HOW SHARPER THAN A CHILE'S TOOTH TO HAVE A THANKLESS SERPENT.

IF YOUSE IS RUNNIN' FOR THE *EXPRESS* IT LEFT EARLY *YESTERDAY.*

WHAT *FOR?* WE HAD SEATS *REE*SERVED.

RIGHT UNDER THE *REEFRIG-AN-ATOR* CAR.

IT HAD TO LEAVE YESTERDAY 'CAUSE IT'S DUE IN **FORT MUDGE** TOMORROW.

A FIVE MILE TRIP!

I *KNOW!* BUT FORT MUDGE IS HARD TO FIND... GOIN' CROST-COUNTRY 'SPECIALLY.

WHAT TRAIN *DON'T* GO CROSS-COUNTRY?

WITHOUT TRACKS?

CHAPTER
17

A Mouse Traps
And Trips

WHO'S THE TAD WITH THE BABY RATTLE, SNAVELY?

A ANGLE WORM SCAPER WHAT I PICKED UP IN *WESTWEGO*.... WANTS TO LEARN SNAKIN' AND SERPENTIN'...

HE WANTS TO BE A *RATTLER*, I S'POSE?

NO.....HE SAYS IT MAKES HIM SHAKEY HEARIN' THINGS RATTLE AHIND OF HIM ....BUT HE'S GOTTA LEARN *ALL* BRANCHES ...

WHEN HE'S THRU WITH *THIS* STEP HE GOTTA TRY BEIN' A *ADDER* THO' HIS MA SAY HE'S WEAK ON 'RITH*METICKS* AN' STUFF.....AN' AFTER *THAT,* HE GITS A TRY AS A APPRENTICE COBRA.

HOODED?

SHUCKS NO! HE AIN'T SHAMED OF BEIN' A *SNAKE!* HE GONE COME RIGHT OUT WITH IT---- *ACTUAL HE'D MAKE A NICE HOOP SNAKE* BUT THEY IS BEEN RULED *MYTH-OLOGICAL BEASTS* AN' IS DISQUALIFIED IN ALL STATES EAST OF THE ROCKIES.

NOW IF YOU'LL JES' HOLD THAT AN' *FINGER* THE HOLES I'LL BLOW THE *APPRENTICE COBRA* A FEW CHORUSES OF RIMSKY KORSA-KOFF AN' LEARN HIM A JIG.

RIGHTO, SNAVELY.

SNAVELY, YOU IS BLOWIN' MORE *ANNIE LAURIE* AN' THE KID IS DOIN' THE HIGHLAND FLING!

IF YOU WANTS TO SHOW **SNAVELY** HOW A **MONGOOSE** TACKLES A **COBRA** WHYN'T YOU DEMONSTRATE WITH THE **WORM CHILD?**

YEH...

I DON'T WANNA PICK ON A INFANT.

YOU DON'T **HAF**TA BE ROUGH. JES' SHOW US **GENTLE-LIKE...**

THE KID'S READY.

VERY WELL BUT ONLY IN THE INTERST OF **SCIENCE.**

I'LL GO SLOW, KID..... DON'T BE SCAIRT... **EASY** DOES IT.

YESSIR, **EASY**... **EASY**.. **EAAH!**

EASY DOES **IT,** I SAID!

VERY EDUCATIONAL.

HOW'D YOU MANAGE TO GIT THROWN BY THE **WORM CHILE?**

SHEER SKILL! BESIDES, MY FOOT SLIPPED.

HOWEVER, I'LL GO **ON** WITH THE DEMONSTRATION ...... I'LL BE **EASY** ON THE **TAD** WHILST SHOWIN' HOW A **MONGOOSE** TACKLES A COBRA ---**EN GARDE.**

116

NOW, I WAS JUS' GOIN' LIKE **THIS** WHEN-- ooOW---

--OWP!

YOU BULLY! PICKIN' ON THAT LI'L' SMALL WORMCHILE, **THOU BEAST!**

BEAST! BULLY! OGRE! BESTING A CHILE THAT WAY!

I WAS **ONLY** TRY AN' TO TEACH THE WORM CHILE A FEW----

A **BIG STRONG MAN** LIKE **YOU** MAKIN' A **FOOL** OF THAT LI'L' **FELLA---** BOXIN' HIM SILLY WITH A **BLINDIN' DISPLAY** OF FISTIC ARTISTRY!

HE THRUN ME TWO OUT OF **TWO**, MIZ BEAVER, **HONEST!**

SSH---SH--- I KNOW---(HE WAS BEATIN' YOUR EARS OFF ---SHSH---HERE'S YOUR COAT AN' STICK! THOUGHT I BETTER GIT YOU OUTEN THERE----)

(BUT IT DON'T PAY TO LET THEM OTHER MENS KNOW.) **OH, THE SECRET MAGIC OF COMBAT SKILL** WHAT YOU TRICKED THAT BOY WITH----! **YOU BRUTE!**

HEAR HER? WE MUST OF MISSED SOMETHIN'. SHE'S A EXPERT.

118

Panel 1:
HEE HOO! NOSSIR..... HE SAY I IS A *GAL*.... A *PERTY* GAL....

EN *VRAI! GOODIES!* WE ARE INVITES *HIM*, THESE *ONE*, TO DINNER. I HAVE MAKE THOSE CHOCOLATE *MOUSSE* AN'.....

Panel 2:
COME BACK! COME BACK! IT AIN'T LIKE WHAT *YOU* THINK, MR. MOUSE!

Panel 3:
HE GOT *SKEERT* OFF...YOU SAID YOU WAS MAKIN' *CHOCOLATE MOUSSE* AN' OFF RUN THAT MR. MOUSE.

HOW INSULT OF HIM, NO?

Panel 4:
ON A NIGHT WHEN WE ARE TO HAVE THE *SOIREE* WITH SING AN' DANCE...HE CANNOT TREAT LADY THESE WAY, HA?

WHUT LADY?

Panel 5:
YOU LADY! THAT ARE *WHO* LADY! HE SHOULD BE *PER-*SUADE *BACK!*

ME? OH...UH..YEH, ME! WODDY YA KNOW?!

Panel 6:
I'LL PERSUADE THE *TAR* OUTEN HIM!

APPEAL TO HIS SENTRYMENTAL SIDE, *NO?*

WOMAN TALKS 'BOUT EATIN' A *CHOCOLATE MOUSSE*, A MAN IN *MY* POSITION CAN'T BE *TOO* CAREFUL.

HATE TO RUN OFF FROM MIZ BEAVER... BUT.. *OH*-- *HEH*LO, MIZ BEAVER.'

I BEEN SETTIN' HERE... CUT THRU TH' BACK WAY... HOPE TO *PER*SUADE YOU TO COME BACK..

YOU AIN'T THE CHOCOLATE MOUSSE WE HAD IN MIND ...*ALL A BIG MISTAKE*-- I BEEN PLAYIN' A GAME A-WAITIN' FOR YOU:

HE LOVE ME.
BANG!
HE LOVE ME NOT.
BANG!
HE LOVE ME.
BANG!

WELL WELL WELL WELL WELL WELL WELL WELL WELL A MISTAKE EH WELL WELL WELL WELL WELL WELL WELL

WELL
WELL
WELL
WELL

YOU KIN SAY *THAT A-*GAIN.

WELL
WELL
WELL
WELL
WELL
WELL

CHAPTER
18

Who Is Now And Ever
Has Been A Member
Of The Tea Party?

NICE OF YOU TO HAVE ME IN FER *DINNER* AFORE YOUR *SOIREE*, LADIES.... I WAS SOIREE-ING AWAY THE EVENIN' WITH THE *PREXY* OF FRANCE JES' *LAST SPRING*, (GOT CAUGHT IN A *DULUTH* LADY'S GRIP AN' WOUND UP IN *PAREE*.)

HOW QUAINTS.

CHOMP.

SHE GUV A *BELLER* WHILST UNPACKIN' HER *DEMITASSELS* AN' OTHER DOODADS..... SO I SCRUMP OUT AN' HOTFOOTED DOWN THE HALL.... MAN SWEEPIN' OUT HIS ROOM LEMME IN AN'.....

I SAYS, "THANKS", AN' HE SAYS TO HIS FRIEND, "HEY, I GOT A TALKIN' MOUSE".... OTHER FELLER SAYS, "YEH, AN' I'M THE PRESIDENT OF FRANCE.".... SO, I UPS TO HIM AN' SAYS "FRANCE BETTER GIT A *GUMMINT*! REMEMBER THE MAN FED A HORSE ONE LESS STRAW A DAY AN' JES' WHEN THE HORSE WAS GITTIN' ALONG WITHOUT--- " *AW!* YOU IS LAUGHIN' AWREADY!

URF UNG UMP GUNCH.

YOU MUSTA HEARD THE STORY AFORE! IT *IS* A REAL ROUSER, AIN'T IT, MIZ BEAVER?

WHO IS LAUGHIN'? *WHAT STORY? I* IS EATIN' *CORN!*

EVENIN', MIZ MA'M'SELLE HEPZIBAH..... EVENIN', MIZ BEAVER .... *HEY, MOUSE.*

WELCOME TO THESE *SOIREE*, M'SIEUR POGO.

YOU'RE JES' IN TIME FER THE REST OF MY STORY 'BOUT *FRANCE*, POGO. PULL UP A CHAIR....

THIS FELLA I RUN INTO HIS ROOM OF, TURNS OUT TO BE A BIG *PER-FUME* MAKER *(THEY PRONOUNCES IT PARAFINE)* WELL, I GIVE HIM A *IDEA*.. A PERFUME LIKE A BREEZE ..OPEN SPACES ... FRESH AIR ... FOR THE *NONCE* CALL IT "*X*:

HE IS *NATURUL DEE*LIGHTED AN' IS COUNTIN' OUT A MILLION IN *ONES* FOR ME WHEN I MENTIONS A GOOD SLOGAN: *USE "X" AND SMELL LIKE ALL OUTDOORS.* ...WELL, RIGHT THEN A *VERY NASTY THING HAPPENS* HE....

HE USED TO TELL THIS'N ABOUT *LOS ANGELES* WHEN *THAT* WAS A TONEY TOWN.

OH, HOW *GAY!* THAT YEAR IN *FRANCE* WAS JUST AFORE THE *BOTTOM* FELL OUT OF THE *MARKET.* I WAS WORKIN' IN THIS FOODSTUFFS EMPORIUM ON THE *RAVIOLI* WHEN I ...

YOU MEAN ON THE *RIVIERA*, NO, M'SIEUR ?

WELL, IF YOU MUST GIVE IT THE *FRENCH* PRONOUNCEMENT...O.K. ANYHOW, *THERE I WAS ON THIS BIG PILE OF CANNED RIVIERA* ....

122

THE **CAT**, WHOM IT WAS **MY** DUTY TO BE CHASED BY, CAME ALONG *SNEERIN'* IN THE MOTHER TONGUE, SO I HOLLERS OUT: *"CAMEMBERT!"* (FRENCH FOR "COME ON, BERT!" THE CAT'S NAME BEIN' *BERTRAM*) WELL, SIR, THAT CAT GUV A LEAP..**WOW!**

OVER WENT THE PILE OF RIVIERA IN A **AWFUL CRASH** .... THE FLOOR SAGGED, QUIVERED, AN' *BOOM! THE BOTTOM FELL OUT OF THE MARKET!* WE ALL LANDED IN THE CELLAR SCREAMIN' GALLICISMS WHICH BRUNG THE GENDARMES ON THE DOUBLE AN'......

HOW 'BOUT "LIZA JANE"?

STOP ME IF I'M **BORIN'** YOU BUT IT'S SUCH A CLEAR NIGHT FOR A GOOD TALK.... WELL, WHEN THAT MARKET ON THE *RUE DE LA CHAT* COLLAPSED IT CAUSED QUITE A **STIR** ..1929 IT WAS...

THE PAPERS WERE FULL OF IT.. PEOPLE SAID: *WHY'D THE BOTTOM FALL OUT OF THE MARKET?* HA! I **KNOW!** THE CAT KNOCKED OVER THE CANNED GOODS. *DID THE EXPERTS ASK ME? NO*, THEY--

THEY MIGHT OF BEEN THINKIN' OF ANOTHER MARKET.

Y'MEAN ANOTHER MARKET COLLAPSED THAT YEAR?

A MARKET ON **WALL STREET.**

A COINCIDENCE! WALL STREET STORE, HUH? SMALL PLACE, NO DOUBT... NEVER HEARD OF IT.

NO, IT HAD A LI'L' SIZE ON IT--- Y'EVER HEAR OF THIS **WALL STREET** WHAT POLITICIANS AN' REEVOLUTIONARY RASCALS IS ALLUS HOLLER'N' *DOWN WITH IT?*

ALWAYS THOUGHT THAT WAS A OL' *MYTHOLOGICAL BEAST*... WODDYA KNOW! WELL, THIS **BIG MARKET COLLAPSE** *I* WAS IN WAS ᴡᴍ.

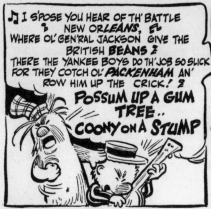

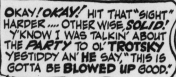

OKAY! **OKAY!** HIT THAT "SIGHT" HARDER..... OTHER WISE, **SOLID!** Y'KNOW I WAS TALKIN' ABOUT THE **PARTY** TO OL' **TROTSKY** YESTIDDY AN' **HE SAY,** "THIS IS GOTTA BE **BLOWED UP** GOOD."

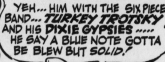

YEH... HIM WITH THE SIX PIECE BAND.... **TURKEY TROTSKY** AND HIS **DIXIE GYPSIES**..... HE SAY A BLUE NOTE GOTTA BE BLEW BUT SOLID!

TROTSKY?

OH, SURE! SOLID BLUE IS MY OWN FAVORITE SHADE.

AS WE QUIETLY TAKE **POGO'S** GRUB, (HE BEING AWAY FROM HOME LIKE THE IRRESPONSIBLE DESPOTIC LANDLORD HE IS,) **I WORRY**.....

YEAH.

PENSACOLA IT'S THE SPA

I WORRY ABOUT A WORLD WHERE AN HONEST MAN NEVER KNOWS **WHO** IT IS **SAFE** TO BE **AGAINST.** ONLY YESTER- DAY I TRUSTED THE TURTLE... WE'D TURNED TO HIS SIDE ....IN FACT, **JOINED 'EM!**

YEAH.

WE KNEW OF HIS **STRATIFIED STUPIDISM**...WE WERE **SURE:** HERE WAS ONE WE COULD BE AGAINST WITH **IMPUNISTIC SECURITISM!** WHAT HAPPENS? HE REVEALS HIS TRUE FACE .... **HE HAS POWERFUL FRIENDS!** WHO **CAN** BE TRUSTED?

YEAH.

STOP LOOKIN' AT ME LIKE THAT.

YEAH.

CHAPTER
19

A Fall Classic
Is Felled

PFAH!

BOXING GLOVES! *WHO NEEDS THESE?*

M'SIEUR ALBERT IS *FOUR-FLUSHER!*

FOUR-FIVE --- YES, EVEN SIX, SEVEN OR *TWELVE FLUSHER!*

WE GONE NEED A **UMPIRE** TO PREVENT *FIGHTS.*

FOOMPH! THEY ALLUS **START** EM.

POGO IS RIGHT. *WE* NEED A *UMPIRE.*

A **ARBITER** WHO IS *TOUGH!* ONE WHO CAN BACK UP HIS OPINION --- AN UMPIRE WITH **COURAGE** --- WITH **STRENGTH! FEARLESS! A REAL FIGHTER! A REAL MAN!** WHO AMONGST US?

𝄞 OH, MIZ BEAVER 𝄽

𝄞 YOO HOO ♫♪

HMPH! AIN'T YOU GOT NOTHIN' IN A MORE DAINTY SIZE ---'BOUT A **NINE**, MEBBE?

UMPIRE

HOPE YOU DON'T MIND ME *PRAC-TICIN'* MY **RADIO JOB**, UNCLE BALD-WIN ---'TAINT HOOKED UP YET, BUT---- HERE GOES : *GOOD AFTERNOON, HERE IS A IMPORTANT PRE-GAME FLASH!*

SEE IT *NOW!* THE **THROBBING NEW FILM** "*CUMQUAT BLOSSOMS*" SEE THE *ALLURIN'* **MIBSIE FARQUHAR**, THE CURVACEOUS AN' *DEE-LECTABLE* **TOO-TOO DEVINE**---*AND* THAT SLOW BURNIN' *TIGRESS*, GREEN-EYED *FOLLY FRISBIE!*

132

WHY AIN'T YOU LETTIN' LI'L' *GRUN-DOON* PLAY IN YO' *WORLD SERIES* NO MORE?

IT'S *OVER*... HE *UN*RAVELED OUR BALL.

IF YOU AIN'T GONE LET HIM PLAY YOU OUGHT TO GIVE BACK HIM HIS BALL.

HE MADE A *HOO-RAW'S NEST* OUTEN IT.

AN' IT *WASN'T* HIS ANYHOWS... HE JES' TRY TO SWAP OFF'N HIS BIG 'UN FER IT.

IF YOU AIN'T GONE LET HIM PLAY WE'LL JES' TAKE THE *BIG* ONE TOO.

I'M SORRY WE EVER LAID A *EYE* ON YO' LI'L' *SCAPER.*

IF YOU AIN'T GONE LET HIM PLAY THEY'S NO *REQUIRE* TO *APOLOGY,* MR. ALBERT. US GROUN'CHUNKS KIN TAKE A *HINT!*

CHAPTER
20

A Tiger Burns
Bright

WHERE?! HA?! DO WE HAVE HEADLINES LIKE **THIS** ANYMORE? MY **FAVORITE** KIND?...**NO!** THEY **BURY** THINGS!

PAPERS PRINT THE NEWS WHAT **IS**...NOT JES' WHAT YOU **WANTS**. WODDYA MEAN THEY **BURY** THINGS?

HERE'S A PAPER (WRAPPED 'ROUND A FISH) AUG. 29 1953. **BURY THINGS?!** LOOK WHERE THEY PUT **DETROIT** IN THE STANDIN'S...**SEVENTH PLACE!** 40 GAMES BURIED! THAT DIDN'T HAPPEN IN **MY** DAY, FRIENDS!

IT'S **MY** CONTENTION, FRIENDS, IF WE HAD A **TRULY** LIBERAL PRESS THE **TIGERS** WOULD OF GOT A BETTER SPOT IN THE **AMERICAN LEAGUE STANDINGS**...SUCH THINGS ARE NOT THE **WHIM OF CHANCE**...

THEY IS THE 'WHIM OF WHAMMY.

OL' ROY MATSON

FORGET SPORTS...**TAKE THEM COMICKAL** STRIPS...A NEWS PAPER BUYS A STRIP AN' WILL IT LET OTHER PAPERS IN THE SAME TOWN HAVE IT, TOO?

HA! TALK ABOUT FREEDOM.

ROY MATSON

BESIDES.... **WHO..WHAT PITIFUL PITTANCE READS THE PAPERS TODAY?**

WELL, THERE'S A WAY OVER 50,000,000 COPIES EVER'DAY READ BY, AT THE VERY LEAST, TWO PEOPLE APIECE.

WELL, YOU DON'T HAVE TO **SNAP** MY HEAD OFF.

DIN'T KNOW IT WAS MADE OF RUBBER, SON.

HUMPH!

LAST TIME A PAPER MENTIONED ME THEY SPELT MY NAME WRONG.

SEE, YOU IS FUSSIN' 'BOUT A FREE PRESS AN' THE MINUTE THEY MAKES **FREE** WITH YO' NAME, YOU GITS **MAD.**

CRITTURS IS **ALL** ALIKE.

WHAT MAKES YOU SO TALKY? THEM'S THE **FIRST** WORDS YOU SAID SINCE **WENSDAY.**

I BEEN MULLIN' AT 'EM.

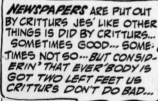

NEWSPAPERS ARE PUT OUT BY CRITTURS JES' LIKE OTHER THINGS IS DID BY CRITTURS... SOMETIMES GOOD... SOMETIMES NOT SO.... BUT CONSIDERIN' THAT EVER'BODY IS GOT **TWO LEFT FEET** US CRITTURS DON'T DO BAD...

I FIGGERS, PORKY, THAT **EVERY MAN'S HEART IS EVENTUAL** IN THE **RIGHT PLACE.**

AN' I FIGGERS POGO, THAT IF A MAN'S GONNA BE **WRONG** 'BOUT SOMETHIN' **THAT** IS THE **BEST** WRONG THING TO KEEP BEIN' WRONG ABOUT, 'TIL **FOREVER.**

137

CHAPTER
21

An Episode That
Goes Off Half Cockney

I S'Y, ALF, IF IT AIN'T ONE OF THEM, NOW, 'EDGEHOG CHAPS.

RIGHTO, REGGIE... 'EY GUV'NOR, WHICH WAY TO THE CRICKET MATCH?

COR! 'E'S COLD GRAVY, ALF; 'E NEVER EARD OF THE GYME, BY THE LOOK OF 'IM.

THE ROUNDER SERIES FOR THE WORLD CUP, Y'KNOW!'

ALF, LAD, IF YOU 'TYKE NOTE, 'E'S WEARIN' A GRASS KILT. LUMME! S'POSE 'E'S A HAWAIIAN?

IF 'E IS... 'E'S A LYDY... AN' ME WITH ME TOPPER ON.

COO! 'E'S NO HAWAIIAN... WHERE'S HIS GUITAR AN' 'IS BLINKIN' PINE-APPLE?

(AS I S'Y, REGGIE, 'E'S A FEMYLE... THEY DON'T CARRY THEM.) A THOUSAND PARDONS, MADAM.

THINK I'LL GO BACK.... 'LONG AS HE SAID WHAT HE SAID ....

ONE OF YOU IS SAID TO ME... "A THOUSAN" PARDONS, MADAM." SO... HOW ABOUT 'EM?

BLINK ME EYE, IF SHE AIN'T A TALKER AT THAT, REGGIE...... RIGHTO, MA'M. WHAT ABOUT 'EM AS YOU SAYS, MADAM?

140

I DID IT... OH, I JOLLY WELL DID IT...1000 PARDONS...AN' NOBODY WERE PAYIN' *TUPPENCE* TO ME... OWH! FOR SHYME!

PER'APS Y'D GIVE A BIT OF A WORD ON *'OW COME* Y'RE BRUISED AGYNE, 'EY?

I AIN'T NO LADY.

COR! NOW *THAT'S* 'ARDLY A SURPRISE, MUM!

THE SHYMEFUL WY WE *BEEN* TREATED! OW! BETR'YED AGYNE BY A PRETTY FYCE!

IT'S BEEN A *BUSY, BUSY* WEEK, CHURCHY.

JES' UNLAX WHILST I READS THIS JOKE: MAN SAY TO A *SEE-GAR STORE INDIAN*, "DON'T YOU GIT TIRED BEIN' ON YOUR FEET ALL DAY?"

AN'..*HAW!!*..THE INDIAN SAY, "NO, I NEVER...*OOMF WUF WUF* HOO ...I NEVER COULD *STAND* SITTIN' DOWN ANYHOW! HOWF..WOW WOW WHEE! A REAL ROUSER! REAL!

IF YOU AIN'T BUSY, POGO, I'LL TELL YOU A *ROUSER*... A SEEGAR STORE INDIAN SAY: *"I NEVER* COULD BEAR TO SIT ALL DAY." AN' A MAN SAY: "*DON'T YOUR FEET GIT TIRED? STANDIN'*, THAT IS?"

THAT'S THE FUNNY PART----THERE IS MORE BUT I FORGIT IT---- NOT AS FUNNY NEITHER.

WHAT YOU TOLE UP TO NOW WAS JES' *FINE*... WANNA GO ON HOME FOR COOKIES AN' MILK?

CHAPTER
22

A Scandal
For School

That's **FINE**, you li'l' worm chillun... you spelled "IS"-- now see kin you all spell "CAT."

NOTHIN' TO IT, UNCLE POGO.

LET'S SEE.. YEP... C...A...T... **RIGHT!** THAT **IS** "CAT."

ANOTHER **SHAMEFUL** EXHIBITION OF THE EDUCATIONAL LEVEL..... THEY SPELLED IT UPSIDE DOWN.

IT'S **HARDER** THAT WAY....

NONETHELESS, I GONNA OPEN A **SCHOOL!** EVER'BODY HERE IS **TOO** IGNORANT....

PHOO.... IT WAS **YOU** SAID THE POEM WHAT OL' CHURCHY HAD WAS AWFUL.... SAID **HE'D** WRIT A BAD ONE.

WHEN **ALL** THE TIME IT WAS A POEM BY **WILL SHAKE-SPEARE**, HIS OWN SELF!

PHMPH! WELL, **HA!** HA-HMM.. YES, WELL! **THAT IS THE VERY TYPE OF IGNORANCE OF WHICH I DE-PLORE!**

ALBERT, I IS THINKIN' 'BOUT OPENIN' A SCHOOL.

I ALLUS **THUNK** YOU NEEDED A LI'L' MORE **LEARNIN'**, OWL.

DON'T GO BE **SOURGRASSTIC.** ALL KIN LEARN ---- FOR **INSTINCT**, SIR, DOES YOU KNOW THAT **'EL LAGARTO'** MEANS ----

A SEEGAR?

ALLIGATOR! WHERE?

PUT ME DOWN, YOU LUMPHEAD! *YOU IS A ALLIGATOR YOUR OWN SELF!*

SAY, THAT *IS* TRUE, AIN'T IT... IT'S HARD TO REMEMBER ALL OF A SUDDEN LIKE THAT.

ONE THING I KIN TEACH EVER'BODY IN SCHOOL IS 'BOUT **ATOMICAL POWER** AN' INTERNATIONAL POLITINKS

HEY, HOWLAN', I HEAR TELL YOU GONE OPEN UP A SCHOOL.

YEP, I GONE EX-PLAIN THEM ATOMICALS AN' FISSION.. ALSO FUSION, *PRO* AN' *CON.*

HOW 'BOUT **BOTANY?** YOU EVER SEE HOW LIMA BEANS IS FAT AN' ROUNDY..

AN' STRING BEANS IS STRINGY AN' WAX BEANS IS WAXEY AN' CHILE BEANS IS CHILLY? *WHAT MAKES THEM DIFFERMINTS IN BEANS, OWL?*

I DON'T RIGHTLY KNOW, PORKY, BEIN' BUSY AS I IS WITH **ATOMS** AN' THE **WORLD** AN' ALL.....

WULL, *OKAY...* GO 'HEAD BUT I BE *DOGGED* IF I KIN FIGGER HOW YOU ALL KIN 'SPLAIN 'BOUT **ATOMS** AND HOW TO BLOW UP EVER'THIN' AN' *YOU DON'T EVEN KNOW* **BEANS!**

145

OL' **OWL** GONE OPEN UP A **SCHOOL,** HOUN' DOG.

GREAT NEWS! YES, **INDEED.**

MY SCHOOL DAYS... THE GOLDEN YEARS IN FIRST GRADE WERE GONE TOO SOON... I'VE OFT WONDERED WHAT HAPPENED TO OUR MANUAL TRAININ' TEACHER AN' **FOOTBALL** COACH..

A **GREAT GUY,** HUH?

A **LADY**... MISS **BOOMBAH**... WE LOVED HER LIKE A BROTHER...CALLED HER "**SIS**"...WE HAD A CHEER FOR SPORTING CONTESTS..." **YAY WILLACOOCHIE! GLORIOUS WILLACOOCHIE EVER TRUE! FIGHT ON, CHARTROOS AN' PLAID!**

WILLACOO-CHEEE! SIS BOOMBAH.'" WE **ALWAYS** TACKED **HER** ON THE **END.** SHE HOLLERED LOUDER'N ANYBODY...

I SHOULDA **THUNK** SHE WOULD

THIS NOW, **SCHOOL**.....SOON'S I GIT ANOTHER **BENCH** MADE IT'S GONE BE A **SURE 'NUFF U**-NIVERSITY...

GOOD FOR **IT!'**

I'LL HELP YOU TEACH ALL 'BOUT MY **SPECIALTY**.... BECAUSE I IS A **EXPERT** ON MY SPECIALTY..... **AN'** IS A **SPECIALIST** ON IT TOO BESIDES.

YOUR STUDENT BODY IS *PREE-PARED* TO GIVE YOU *TEMPORARY UNDERPINNIN'*, PROF.

THEN YOU KIN GIT OVER TO YOUR *AUNTIE'S*...... *MIZ MYRTLE* IS BOUND TO REMEMBER HOW TO GIT YO' LEG BONES *OUTEN* YO' SHELL ..... *EASY NOW*....

GOT HIM....

OKAY... NORTH BY NORTH EAST-EAST BY WEST-SOUTH-WEST MEN... *BRISK!*

PHOO...MOST DANGEROUS THING I COULD GET WOULD BE *MORE* HELP LIKE *THAT*.

GOOD NEWS, OWL! *GOOD NEWS!* WE IS COMIN' OVER TO *JOIN YOUR FACULTY!*

WHOOOP! KEERFUL.

IS YOU FOLKS COMIN' TO *SCHOOL?*

YES, YES! WE'RE *ACHIN'* TO START...

WHERE'S THE *STADIUM?* WE GOT THE *BACKFIELD* ALL *FIGGERED* OUT....

NO SPORTS ALLOWED!

149

ANYBODY PLAYIN' **HOOKEY** AIN'T GONE PLAY IT WITH **US**.

AW, **YOU WORMS!**

LET 'EM GO IF THEY DON'T WANT NO FUN.

IS THIS A **PRIVATE** FISHIN' PARTY OR KIN I STOWAWAY AN' **SULK** IN COMFORT?

COME ON ABOARD... YOU IS WELCOME.

'SPECIALLY IF YOU IS A **FISH**.

A **FINE** SCHOOL OL' OWL STARTED....NOBODY IS INTER'STED IN THE **FINE** SIDE ...**OWL** WANTS TO TEACH **FISSION** AN' **FUSION** ...(PRO AN' CON)

ALBERT WANTS TO PLAY FOOTBALL WITH A **TWELVE MAN LINE** AN' A **SIX MAN OUTFIELD**... OL' BEAUREGARD WANTS A **CHICKEN** TO COACH THE TEAM....**MIZ BOOMBAH** BY NAME....

BUT NOBODY LISTENS TO **MY** ALMOND MATER SONG WHICH I SUNG WITH **TEARS IN MY EARS** .... **HOW DID** YOU FELLAS LIKE IT BY THE WAY? I NOTICE YOU WENT OFF QUIET-LIKE ... ...OVERCOME?

WULL .... UH...

YOU SAY BEAUREGARD WANTS TO BRING IN A **CHICKEN**?

CHAPTER
23

A Form Of
Hire Education

I DO DECLARE, POGO, IT'S EXTREMELY DIFFICULT FOR AN ELDERLY BACHELOR GIRL TO MAKE A LIVING; SO I TOOK A JOB WITH DR. *WHIMSEY*...

BY JING! MY OL' FOOTBALL COACH, *SIS BOOMBAH*, UP IN *PROVIDENCE*, ALLUS SAID ROADWORK IS MIGHTY BENEFICIAL...

SPECIALLY IF YOU IS ON THE LAM...

BOOP!

HAVE A CARE, SON, I'M AN *OLD LADY*.. ... SO, AS I SAY, POGO, I'M HELPING DR. WHIMSEY AND....

MISS BOOMBAH!

WHO MIGHT *YOU* BE, PRAY TELL, WHO?

GEE, MISS *BOOMBAH*, DON'T YOU RECOGNIZE AN OLD **STUDENT** FROM UP IN *PROVIDENCE*?

YOU'RE THAT OLD **TROUBLE MAKER** LITTLE ROBBIE HALL ...

OW! I AM NOT!

EITHER OF YOU FISH BAIT LI'L' DIGGERS SEED *HOUN' DOG?*

HE GONE TO *ISTANBUL* OR *O-HIO* OR SOME SUCH *EXOTIC* SPOT.

THERE'S ONE.

OH! IT'S *BUSY* BUSY BUSY BUSY! AS PREXY OF THE COLLEGE I GOT *89* ON THE *FACULTY* AN' *NO* STUDENTS... 'COURSE IT REDUCES THE *CLASS* WORK WHICH *DO* SAVE A LI'L' TIME!

GOT HIM!

KEEPIN' TRACK OF PROFESSORS IS LIKE COUNTIN' *BABY SPIDERS. ON,* IF I HAD TO MESS 'ROUND WITH *STUDENTS* TOO, I'D BE IN A *TIZZY!*

IS YOU TRY AN TO BE *FUNNY* ?

ON A *SATURDAY?* WOON'T THINK OF IT!

RIGHT, OWL... YOU'D *NEVER* GIT ALL THE *DIPLOMAS* SIGNED...

NOR THE *HONORABLE* DEE-GREES TOO.....A BIG FIELD IN ITSELF.

TO SAY NOTHIN' OF THE *DIS*-HONORABLE ONES.

158

CHAPTER
24

Nothing Taught
Here Fearlessly

QUICK! QUICK!

THE TEAM IS AT PRACTICE.

CAPTAIN C GLENN ADDOX

HOT DOG! I DON'T WANT TO MISS THIS! WAIT FOR ME!

YOU'RE JUST IN TIME.

I'M ALL TUNED UP... WHERE'S THE REST OF THE TEAM?

RIGHT OVER THERE, YOUNG MAN. GET THE BEANBAG, PLEASE.

BEANBAG!? AND A TEAM OF BIRDS! HOW CAN WE EVER FACE U.C.L.A.?

OH, THE BIRDS ARE NOT ON THE SQUAD. I HIT BEAUREGARD WITH A LOOSE SACK OF WHITE NAVIES AN' NOW HE'S ALIVE WITH COMMON GRACKLES.

I'LL BRUSH THE BIRDS AN' BEANS OFF, HOUN'DOG, AN' MEBBE YOU'LL EXPLAIN.

WELL, SIS BOOMBAH OFFERED TO COACH THE TEAM ON ACCOUNT SHE COACHED MY FIRST GRADE TO THE CHAMPEENSHIP FIVE YEAR STRAIGHT!

POOT

BUT HOW COME YOU IS COVERED WITH BEANS? WHAT WILL NOTER DAME SAY WHEN WE SHOWS UP PLAYIN' BEANBAG!?

160

THAT'S WHY SIS IS A *GENIUS!* THERE'S THE *IRISH* LINED UP... READY TO PLAY *FOOTBALL!*

BUT *WE* TAKE THEM BY *SURPRISE!*

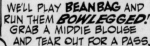

WE'LL PLAY *BEANBAG* AND RUN THEM *BOWLEGGED!* GRAB A MIDDIE BLOUSE AND TEAR OUT FOR A PASS, ALBERT.

*DOG*GONE, COACH, I'LL BE THE *LAUGHIN' STOCK* OF THE *ROSE BOWL!*

WE'LL *MORE* LIKELY GO INTO THE *ORANGE BOWL*... ON ACCOUNT IT'S *CLOSER.*

I JUST *AIN'T* GONNA PUT ON *NO* MIDDIE BLOUSE!

THEN TURN IN YOUR SNEAKERS?

YOU MEAN I GOTTA WEAR A *GIRL'S* SAILOR-SUIT TO BE ON THE *TEAM?*

BIG TIME BEAN BAG REQUIRES CORRECT ATTIRE! MIDDIE BLOUSE AND BLOOMERS ARE A *MUST!*

WELL, OKAY... MIDDIE BLOUSE, BUT *NO* BLOOMERS.

NO BLOOMERS --!?--! YOU'LL LOOK *RIDICULOUS!*

WHY NOT A **LIBERRY**? WE **ALREADY** IS LOADED WITH **COMIC BOOKS**. A HAN'SOME BIG EDIFICE TO HOUSE THE COLLECTION WOULD ----

AS GENERAL **JUSTIN WILSON** SAYS, "REMEMBER DEMOCRATIC **DEE**-MAND..." A STADIUM WILL HOLD 60,000 SCREAMIN' **CASH** CUSTOMERS...

STRANGE.

INDEED.

BUT **WHO** EVER SAW 60,000 SOULS THROWIN' DOWN HARD MONEY TO STAMPEDE INTO A **LIBERRY**?!

I SEE WHAT IT IS ..... SOMEBODY IS BEEN DRAWIN' MUSTACHES ON THE **QUEENS**.

SO THAT'S WHERE THEM QUEENS BEEN GOIN'.

Hum ---- The school is in a football huddle -- strong minds in strong bodies --- **Excellent** --

A QUESTIONABLY **THOUGHTLESS** INNOCUNISTIC REMARK, DEACON; DO YOU KNOW WHERE THIS SEEMINGLY **HARM-LESS** GAME WAS **INVENTED**?

South Bend ----? New Haven? Altoona ----?

IT WAS SMUGGLED OUT OF LOWER BLAGOVESHCHENSK

BY DROME-DARY!

?

THAT WAS THE BASEBALL MAN, YOU TOOL OF THE **ICONOCLASSES**! ABNER (**PAPA**) DROMEDARY!

Hmmm -- Wonder what they're whispering about in that huddle?

YOU'RE RIGHT... IT IS **QUITE** A CONSPIRACY...

164

Who Really
Invented Nothing?

WHILST THE *BEAN BAG* SCRIMMAGE IS GOIN' ON, I COME TO ASK KIN I CARRY YO' BOOKS TO SCHOOL, MIZ MA'M'SELLE HEPZIBAH...

BUT I AM NOT GO, M'SIEUR...

THUNK YOU'D TEACH FRENCH.... *EVER'BODY ELSE IS GONE TEACH....* 'CEPT *ME.* I BRUNG YOU A COUPLE APPLES IN CASE YOU *WAS...*

BUT, NOW I ARE NOT... ...SO *NO* FRUIT? NO?

NAW... NO HARD FEELIN'S..... GUESS I'LL TEACH IT MYSELF. SO I'LL HELP YOU EAT YO' APPLES WHILST I THINKS UP SOME FRENCH TO TEACH.

BUT YOU DO NO MAKE UP THE FRENCH. IT IS *ALL* READY TO GO....ALL IS TO DO IS HEAT HIM AN' SERVE.

WHAT!? I ALLUS THOUGHT YOU WAS JES' MESSIN' AROUN' INVENTIN' THAT FRENCH OUTEN YO' OWN LI'L' HEAD..... SO YOU REALLY *DIN'T* MAKE IT ALL UP, HUH?

NO, ALAS, IF I OWN THE COPYRIGHT OF FRENCH I WOULD BE VER' *WEALTHEE* FELLOW.

GREAT *NEWS*, FELLOWS! I HAVE BOOKED A GAME WITH *IGLOO U.* FROM UP IN THE *TUNDRA.*

GREAT! NEXT STOP: THE *ROSE BOWL!*

FIRST WE MUST CONQUER CALIFORNIA!

AAH... WE'LL TAKE 'EM *EASY!*

HEAR *THAT?*

168

169

WELL, I'LL BE **DOGGED!** NOT A **PEEP**, HUH?

NARY A! SO OLD PETER INVENTED SPANISH FOR SPAIN, CHINESE FOR CHINA, ENGLISH FOR THE **U.S.** AND **A** --- AND **ALL** LIKE THAT THERE...

BLESS MY SOUL.... THEN THEY COULD **ANSWER BACK** ON THE CABLE, HUH?

WELL, HE HAD TO INVENT A CODE FOR **ANSWERING** --- CALLED IT, NATURAL, THE **RE-MORSE** CODE...... **NEXT** THEY NEEDED ELECTRICITY, SO CZAR IVAN TOOK A KITE AND SOME STRING AND A KEY

YOU SAY THE **DEACON** IS AGAINST OUR ACTIVITIES?

SAYS HE DON'T COMPREHEND. 'EM, COACH.

COME SEE HIM, COACH BOOMBAH, AN' **WOO** THE OL' BUZZARD.

MM.. EVERY TIME I **WOO** A MAN HE FOLDS IN THE STRETCH. MEN HAVE NO **DEFENSE** AND LITTLE STAMINA.

NO, I MEAN BE **NICE** TO HIM... MAKE HIM **BUSINESS MANAGER** OF THE **BEAN BAG TEAM** ...... THINK HOW HAPPY HE'LL BE, COUNTIN' THE HOUSE WHEN YOU PLAY **IGLOO U.**

FROM WHAT I HEAR OF THE **DEACON** HE'S TOO LAZY TO COUNT TO **SEVEN** ON HIS **FINGERS.**

I **DUNNO**, MOST BUSINESS MANAGERS KIN BE VERY HAPPY COUNTIN' UP TO **SEVEN** OR EE-**LEVEN** ON THEIR HANDS AN' KNEES,

THE HON. FRED W. GIESEL

171

CHAPTER
26

The Carols

Ground Out . . .

First Bass To

Short

174

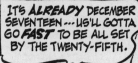

IT'S *ALREADY* DECEMBER SEVENTEEN --- US'LL GOTTA GO *FAST* TO BE ALL SET BY THE TWENTY-FIFTH.

MAN! WHAT'S THE MATTER WITH THEM *GROWED-UPS*? *I* DON'T GIT TUNED UP IN A *RUSH!* I BEEN READY FOR 357 DAYS! *MAN AN' BOY!*

QUIET, YOU TADS. ALL RIGHT, NOW, FIRST: *"HERE WE GO A-WAFFLIN'."* HIT IT!

ӨMX.

WURF.

WANG A BLANG WAM A SOCK

WODDYA THINK OF *THAT* ONE, CHURCHY?

HARD FOR ME TO SAY-- I THINK I'M *TOO CLOSE* TO IT---

HOW 'BOUT US PLAYIN' *HOOKEY* FROM CAROL PRACTICE AN' GOIN' ON A *EXPEDITION?*

YOU BOTH KNOWS THE WORDS TO THE *"TWELVE DAYS OF CHRISTMAS"* AN' ALL?

GBNX.

WURF WURF.

I **THOUGHT** SO... MAM SAYS **CHILLUNS** IS THE SINGLE TYPE CRITTURS WHAT IS **ALWAYS** PREE-PARED FOR CHRISTMAS... IF CHRISTMAS WAS DECLARED ON **FOURTH OF JULY**... **US** WOULD BE **READY!**

GROWED FOLKS IS THE **ONLY** ONES WHAT GOTTA PRACTICE UP GITTIN' IN THE **MOOD**... SPRING **DEC.25** ON 'EM SUDDEN AN' HALF WOULDN'T HAND OUT THEIR **RIGHT NAMES.**

WHY ISN'T YOU TADS PRACTICIN' UP FOR CHRISTMAS LIKE ALL THE OTHERS?

SHUCKS, US CHILLUN IS BEEN READY **ALL** THE **WHOLE YEAR.**

READY FOR WHAT EVER COMES, HUH? Y'ALL KIN **SPELL** YO' NAME GOOD SO'S WHEN YOU SEES A PACKAGE TAGGED FOR **YOU** YOU'LL OPEN IT RIGHT QUICK...

YOU BETCHA!

AN' ALL YEAR YOU SHOWED YO' MAMS AN' PAPS, YO' UNCLES, AUNTS AN' KIN THAT THE WORLD IS REALLY A PLACE OF LOVE BY BEIN' SWEET TO 'EM --- KEEPIN' 'EM AS READY FOR CHRISTMAS AS YOU IS? HELPIN' 'EM GIT THROUGH?

WELL...

WELL... THINK THERE'S STILL TIME TO GIVE 'EM A HAND THAT WAY, UNCLE PORKY?

AW... THERE'S **ALLUS** TIME FOR IT PROVIDIN' YOU DON'T WASTE NONE OF IT.

176

UNCLE PORKY'S *RIGHT!* IT'S ONLY **FAIR** FOR US TADS TO HELP OUR *MAMS* AN' *PAPS* INTO THE **PROPER CHRISTMAS MOOD!**

CAROL NUMBER THREE NOW... EVERYBODY *QUIET*... ONE TWO THREE...

HEY MA!

DECK US ALL WITH **BOSTON CHARLIE,** *WALLA WALLA WASH.,* AN' *KALAMAZOO!* NORA'S FREEZIN' ON THE *TROLLEY,* SWALLER **DOLLAR** CAULIFLOWER 'N **ALLEY-GA-ROO!**

THAT WAS FOR *NOTHIN'*... SO WATCH OUT.

WHILST CHURCHY IS LOOKIN' UP A NEW CAROL, US KIN *REE*-LAX WITH A LI'L' SNACK.

GOOD MORROW, KIND SIRS... WE IS LI'L' *WASS'LERS,* WASS'LIN' LIKE GOOD FELLAS... US WASSAILS WHILE YOU WAITS.

NO NO.. WE IS THE WAITS.

RIGHT HE IS...· WE IS LI'L' **ENGLISH WAITS**... WOULDST WE WHISTLE UP A WASSAIL, WENCESLAS?

BACK OFF'N THE LUNCH!

NOW, ALBERT.

JA, MEIN STADT- HOLDER. LET'S US WASSAIL 'EM TO A FALL.

FREE STYLE.

177

AN' SO ALL TO BED ......

DUNNO *WHY* I BOTHER WITH THIS YEAR AFTER YEAR... *HALLOO!* WAKE UP! *CHRISTMAS EVE!*

OH ... IT'S *YOU*, PORKY... DON'T YOU KNOW YOU AN' ME IS FILLED THE STOCKIN'S AN' JES' FINISH TRIMMIN' THE *TREES*? *IT'S FOUR A.M.*

SO .... YOU DON'T *NEED A WATCH?*

THAT'S GOOD, 'CAUSE HERE'S SOMETHIN' I BEEN SAVIN' FOR YOU SINCE *AUGUST*... NOW, PLEASE, DON'T *FAWN* ON ME .... *A SPRIG OF LOVE-IN-IDLENESS* ---'TAIN'T MUCH, **BUT,** THE WAY FOLKS TREATS EACH OTHER NOW-A-DAYS ....

..IF I LEAVES THIS UP TO *ANY BODY ELSE,* YOU'LL BE LUCKY IF YOU RECEIVES A *SIMPLE GOOD MORNIN'!*

AW ... YOU OL' *PORKYPINE* --- *I DO* B'LEEVE I'LL WAKE UP AN' MAKE COCOA AN' PEANER BUTTER SAN'WICHES.

One Final Word
Leads To Another

WHAT'S YOU GONNA DO WITH THE *OLD* YOU?

BEIN' *PUBLIC* SPIRITED, I IS LEAVIN' *THEM* RE-MAINS TO *HARVARD*. A GIFT...FREE...A BOON TO SCIENCE.

YOUR BRAIN *ALONE* WILL BE WORTH *EVERY* SINGLE PENNY.

THE FELLA YOU USED TO BE, THE OLD YEAR MODEL ...IT'S A THING OF THE PAST? YOU RESOLVES TO BE COMPLETE *NEW*?

ALL NEW AN' *NOBLE* TRAITS .... NO *HOLDOVERS!* A *CLEAN*, FRIEND, SWEEP.

IN SOME WAYS *THAT* IS LIKE CLEANIN' THE *AEGEAN* STABLES AFTER THE HORSE IS BEEN STOLE.

WELL, TIDY IS AS TIDY DO.

TIDY DEW?

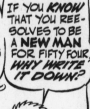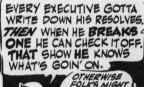

RIGHT, TIDY DEW. *'HINKY DINKY TIDY DEW...':* A OLD SONG WHAT COUSIN CANUTE USE TO SING COME HIGH TIDE, LOW OR PERIGEE.

IF YOU *KNOW* THAT YOU REE-SOLVES TO BE A *NEW MAN* FOR FIFTY FOUR, *WHY WRITE IT DOWN?*

EVERY EXECUTIVE GOTTA WRITE DOWN HIS RESOLVES. *THEN* WHEN HE *BREAKS ONE* HE CAN CHECK IT OFF. *THAT* SHOW HE KNOWS WHAT'S GOIN' ON.

OTHERWISE FOLK'S MIGHT DOUBT HIM.

THIS NEW MAN YOU IS GONE BE.... *WHO IS HE?* WHO YOU GONE *BE?*

OH... MEBBE I'LL BE PRESIDENT **GRANT**... I HEAR HE GOT A BIG PLACE UP ON RIVERSIDE DRIVE... RENT FREE*!*

NO...THAT JOB IS BEEN DONE...YOU GOTTA BE A *BRAN'NEW* SOMEBODY.

WODDYA MEAN THE JOB'S *DONE?* THERE'S STILL A *DEE*-MAND.... **STILL ROOM** AT THE TOP, MY FRIEND.

YOU WON'T LIKE BEIN' UP ON THAT DRIVE...TOO MANY CARS...TOO MUCH **TRAFFIC**...

THEN I COULD SET UP AS A *TRAFFIC COP.* THINK OF THE BUSINESS I'D GET*!*

YOU'D GET THE BUSINESS AN' YOU'D **DESERVE** IT.... UH, HOW CAN YOU TEAR YOURSELF AWAY, POGO?

YOU GOT A REASON TO LEAVE?

NO---- BUT I'LL THINK OF SOMETHIN'

CHURCHY BEEN TALKIN' TO **BUN RABBIT**...CLAIMIN' HE'S GONE BE A NEW MAN BUT CAN'T FIGGER WHO...

HERE HE COME...HE LOOK JES' LIKE **LAST** YEAR AN' EVEN MORE LIKE THE ONE AFORE THAT.

DID YOU AN' OL' BUN DECIDE WHO YOU'S TO BE FOR THE NEW YEAR?

I TURNED HIM OFF WITH A *OLD JEST*...TOLE HIM I IS GONE BE A *APPLE SELLER* SEEIN' AS IT MOUGHT BE A RAGE.

HOW'S *THAT?* IT'S ALREADY HOLDIN' QUITE A NUMBER... LIL' CARD IN IT SAY: *NO. 7,316,492.*

'TAIN'T THE KINDA NUMBER I HAD IN MIND.

HAD IN MIND A NUMBER OF CRITTURS BEIN' IN IT, FOR TO *EN-*JOY THE GAME.

BOLIVAR, MY YOUNG 'UN, HAD A *BOWL FULL* OF *FLEAS* YESTIDDY... MUST OF BEEN A BILLION, GIVE OR TAKE A MILLION ---A CRAZY CROWD... THE JOINT WAS JUMPIN'.

I GOT OUR *SCHOOL SONG* ALL WROTTEN. IT GOT A *FIERCE LILT* ON IT--- WANNA HEAR IT?

DON'T YOU WANT A BOWL ALREADY FILLED WITH *SPECKLE-*TATORS, POGO?

NO!

WHAT? AFTER I SPENT ALL *NIGHT* PUTTIN' IN *BRAN' NEW ARPEGGIOS* AN' A WHOLE *DOUBLE APPOGIATURA* TO SAY *NOTHIN'* OF A BIG HOT *PIZZACATO*.....

WHAT?

WHERE?

MY LIFE WORK IS *SPURNT*... *HOW RAW! HOW RUE!* HE SAYS "*NO!*" *HOW RAW!*

WHAT'S HE CHEERIN' FOR?

MEBBE FOR MR. ARPEGGIO OR THAT, NOW, HOT *PIZZACATATO.* I DON'T SEEM TO SEE 'EM THO'...

HOW RAW! HOW RUE!

WHO FOR *HOWRAW?* HOWROO FOR WHO?

NOBODY IN THERE EXCEPT *DOMESTIC FLEAS,* BUT NONE IS TAKIN' A BOW OR EVEN BATTIN' A EYE.

186

187

THE ESTATE

OF

OUR INDEPENDENCE

Sculling alertly through the waters of a Sunday afternoon we listen to the radio reports, hurried to our anxious ears through the driving rain, reports of drownings, highway accidents, death by design, explosions of small boys. When the clamor has died and is replaced by the soothing strains of George M. Cohan played upon organ and drum, the soft voice of man's best friend, his wife, observes: "Holiday rain. All those people died for nothing. . . . At least they might have had better weather for it."

And indeed they might have. In fact, we might all have better weather as we jostle toward the finish. Too soon we breast the tape and too late we realize the fun lay in the running. We deny that the end justifies the means without ever stopping to consider that for practical purposes the End and the Means are one and the same thing. If there is to be any satisfaction in life it must come in transit, for who can tell when he will be struck down in mid-method?

So, as we speed along, running up our colors and running down our neighbors, it might be well to avoid being hoist by our own halyards. In this Era of the Boomerang it is easy to counter suspicion with suspicion. It is not quite as easy to return hate for love but many of us manage it through the simple procedure of viewing all love with the suspicion reserved for the unknown. This is unfortunate because love takes many

189

forms, (not all of them immediately identifiable and therefore even more suspect.) One of these forms is humor.

Naturally the humorist in any age is viewed with some misgivings for he plays with no particular team. He performs the duties of a busy-body umpire who may be expected to hit, run, field the ball and call himself out on a close play at home. The fact that he may work equally well and equally often for all teams does not make him any more dependable. He is not to be trusted.

These very thoughts are highly suspicious because it has long been the cheerful habit of nearly every American to think fondly of himself as a humorist. And, with his flair for irreverence, his social impudence, his unblinking recognition of the truth, the American, by and large over the centuries, has been a humorous man.

Currently we have narrowed our formula for the joke down to a safe channel alive with harbor lights, bell buoys, constant soundings from the bow, shouted warnings from the shore, signal fires and manned life-boats. Such channeled activity can become ritual.

A form of ritualistic humor crept into the habits and ceremonies of the ancient North American Indians. These Original Americans employed at least one comic device (a sure-fire boff), that consisted of several humorists smearing and throwing dung over some selected colleague.

As humor, the act had one serious drawback in that it became impossible, eventually, to embrace the target in a show of good fellowship directly after the performance.

Another Original American is named by a less original American as the authority on Vigilantics who taught that a suspicious man should kick rapidly upon the groin of a suspect until the latter is made helpless. This provides mirth for spectator and raconteur.

All of this good fun, the smearing, the throwing, the kicking, is spoiled when the scape-goat is not a good sport. It is one of the major requirements of joke-function that the butt should either (A.) be quiet or (B.) get lost . . . if he is not already rendered dead.

The Era of the Boomerang is putting our national sense of humor to a severe test. The full import of inventing the world's most devastating weapon was not realized until we learned that the enemy, acting like cads, had swiped the secret. Having been prepared to snigger, we are not prepared to applaud; but neither should we be ready to whimper.

It is not the time for a man to demonstrate the strength of his guts with a belly-laugh, but nevertheless here is a comic situation. It is a comedy in the classic tradition, so near to tragedy that the difference is indiscernible to the participant. This classic comedy is fundamentally that of the Pompous Ass falling on his bulging behind. It is nearly always funny to the onlooker. It is seldom funny to the Pompous Ass. Like it or not, however, the joke remains . . . and it is on us.

So, as we move along, we cannot care who sings our country's songs; beneath the high notes of patriotism, we want to hear the low notes of laughter, always off-key, always true.

Jagged, imperfect and lovely, the goal lies here. This is the estate of our independence.

WALT KELLY